Giles Vickers Jones has just finished presenting the fifth series of ITV At The Movies for ITV1 and ITV2 which was his initial idea and format. He recently presented Playdate, the new interactive dating show on ITV2. Giles has also recently been seen on California Dreaming for T4, living in Hollywood for six weeks as one of five trying to make it in LA. Through this he successfully landed a role presenting for E! Entertainment covering high-profile movie premieres in the UK and which is televised worldwide. Giles co-hosted V and the Reading Festival shows for the ITV Network, interviewing the bands and linking the live performances. He also anchored the late-night show, ITV at the Festivals. After a brief career as a model, Giles began in TV working for the Dating Channel. As well as TV he is about to embark on a major international eco-project www.pixeltrees.com. He has already written two books, ***The Best Day Of My Life*** and ***Professional Modelling*** and this is his third. He has his own film review and Hollywood column in two national celebrity magazines. ***The Seven Worst Men In London*** is in the early stages of becoming a movie.

Seven men, seven stories each, all anonymous, all shocking.
'The Seven Worst Men in London' will make you realise
what you think you know, what you think you've done is
nothing in comparison.
Telling the truth has never been so wrong.

Praise for The Seven Worst Men In London

This book evoked two reactions from me!

Firstly, and this is the official review if my wife is reading this is... what kind of men are these blokes? Totally depraved sex maniacs; as a fellow man I was repulsed by their behaviour. These 'stories', and I wonder just how true they are, are deplorable and do us real men no favours in the eyes of the opposite sex. They should be ashamed of themselves!

That said, and strictly between you and me, I am jealous as hell. These tales are the tales I wish I could regale my mates with... boys, you are living out all our dreams... so have one (or ideally a set of twins) on me!!
Ben Jones
Absolute Radio DJ

SEX, drugs and rock and roll for the modern celeb!

If you thought being a celebrity was all about whoring yourself on red carpets for exposure, think again! This is what whoring really means when you're famous.

This book is so wrong it's so right. Have my own sneaky suspicions who a few of the famous faces are and have made it my mission to find out the rest.

Think Channel 4's Shameless set in the celebrity world and you have a winner on your hands!
James Ingham
Showbiz Journalist Daily Star Sunday

This book is terrible: full of drink, debauchery, filth, sex and perversion by a bunch of degenerates parading as celebrities. You ought to be ashamed of yourselves, all of you, come out of the closet and reveal who you are. This book is the worst… and it's brilliant! No wonder I couldn't put in down.
Dave Berry TV presenter and XFM DJ

I don’t often get to read books due to all the training but, when I do, it’s not often one shocks you to the core and shows you how the other half live. A must read, it takes things to a new level.
James Haskell, England rugby player

I had the privilege of indulging myself in this book during a delayed night flight from Gatwick to New York. I had intended to use the first few chapters to work on my overtired eyelids and put me firmly in the land of nod.

Impossible!

From the outset, the book hooked me firmly on an oh so sweet and salty tasting barb and then reeled me in. My curiosity was aroused (good choice of word, believe me) from the very start as I tried to guess the celebrity behind each perverted but unquestionably true story. Each story is written by our protagonist Giles Vickers Jones, told by each individual, I imagine, during a raucous drink- and drug-fuelled weekend in either Amsterdam, Prague or the good old West End of London where the majority of the tales take place. Vickers Jones does not hold back on the language nor the seriously explicit tales of conquests, threesomes, spit roasts, orgies and downright perverted filth. And neither should he. The book is written so skilfully that you can really imagine sitting at the well-stocked table flowing with alcohol in your all-time favourite bar, somewhere in your dark and distant past with the type of friends you'd die for. The humour of the book is awesome, original boys’ own stuff, a kind of mix between Roy of the Rovers and Debbie does Dallas, with Linda Lovelace looking in from the wings with her mouth full.

The book works wonderfully well and it’s a great 'lads' read. I imagine it will be handed around to girlfriends and wives too, maybe both... Just make sure it's not left around for great Aunty May to pick up.
Ken Scott, author and ghostwriter to the stars

ISBN: 978-1-905988-62-4

Cover by Kelly Leonie Walsh

Published by Libros International

www.librosinternational.com

Printed in Great Britain by
the MPG Books Group, Bodmin and King's Lynn

THE SEVEN WORST MEN IN **LONDON**

Giles Vickers Jones

Acknowledgements

This all started as a seedling of an idea thought up in a pub. In retrospect where else could something like this begin? I was with one of the seven guys a week later, having stewed for seven days over who I should include, and when I mentioned it to him, his exact words were "Hell yeah! That'd be hilarious." As it turned out, his stories were in fact very funny. It's been a relatively simple process ever since. I know this book covers some subjects which are a little out there and for that I thank the honesty of these seven men for telling their stories, although I don't want to lay it on too thick because really, like all men, they just wanted to gloat!

I want to thank each of the seven men because I know that these stories were hard to disclose. In some cases it took some serious coercing while in others it felt like no battle at all. You seven guys were fantastic! I hope you are all pleased with the finished article. Your stories are officially told!

To Ashley Hames, who brilliantly assessed the book, and did one of the most inspired forewords I've read in a long time. Wordsworth would be impressed; to be fair so he should, as Ashley's book ***Sin Cities: Adventures of a Sex Reporter*** is absolutely phenomenal.

Thanks to Si Dent, who gave me support and believed in me at a time when no one else would, and of course Ken and Carol, a truly exceptional editor who never blushed once, well not that I noticed! Plus the team at Libros International our publishers, and Anna my wife who I married while writing this book and who still doesn't know much about the content or which of my friends did the stories!

Enough thanks from me, and if I've missed anyone out, my apologies and thanks to you too...and I'll thank you again in the next book – ***The Seven Worst Women in London***. Then again, we may have already met them…

Thank you

Giles Vickers Jones

Mo, the best in the world.

'The Seven Worst Men in London' is a collection of seven stories as seen through the eyes of those seven men who really are deplorable, not in the sense that they are evil, cruel or criminals, but because the lives they lead are normally only led by the super rich and the über famous.

What makes these men stand apart from any other young men around major cities is that these are the very epitome of the alpha male. There have been books like 'The Game' and TV shows with tips on how to attract the fairer sex. By comparison those are child's play. These men do it on their own terms in their home town to great success.

Whether you agree with the blatant lack of respect for sex, whether or not you like the way these men pick up these women, or whether you can't understand why they feel the need to seduce, the bottom line is they understand themselves and maybe you can understand where they are coming from or maybe you can't. You will however appreciate on some level the amazement at what they get up to.

These anonymous true stories written by famous people in London will leave many thoughts with you, but one thing is certain! You will feel a level of awe and in some cases admiration at the ferocity and aplomb with which they all, in their unique way, seduce the opposite sex!

'Sex without love is a meaningless experience. But as meaningless experiences go, it's one of the best.'

Woody Allen

Foreword by Ashley Hames

I always thought that where sex was concerned I was a seasoned pro.

Until I read this book.

Now, despite being a veteran of hundreds of porn shoots, swingers' parties, fetish nights, orgies and gang bangs, my own debauched history feels like that of an innocent schoolboy. Ever shagged a wife and daughter? Joined the Mile High Club? Had an orgy with multiple hookers in a top London hotel? Fucked two sisters...at the same time? Nope, me neither. The people you will read about in '**The Seven Worst Men In London**' have done all this and far, far more. And, bonus, they're all celebrities.

If *Heat* magazine was top shelf material, then it would read something like this.

This book takes you underneath the bedcovers of some of the most extreme sexual predators on the planet–famous people ruthlessly focused on getting high and getting laid. Laden with cash and confidence, they have access to all the best parties, the most expensive drugs, the hottest girls...and the most mind-boggling sexual experiences.

Jealous? Me too.

From a top model to a pro-golfer, a writer and a pop star, author Giles Vickers Jones has trawled through his celebrity contacts to show us how the other half fuck. And what an eye-opener! This is Prick-Lit at its finest, the exposé that the Editor of *The News of the World* must dream about on a nightly basis – and it's all right here in its full-on, bizarre, hilarious, shocking and utterly depraved glory.
Put it this way – any book that includes the line *'she deep-throated me as I fucking exploded like a white emulsion warhead'* gets the thumbs up from me.

'**The Seven Worst Men in London**' is never going to make it onto the school curriculum but, trust me, in terms of sex education, this is the Fucking Bible. Almost unintentionally (I think they're just showing off) our protagonists shamelessly reveal how to get into a girl's knickers and how best to proceed once we're there. Sure, you and I may lack the kudos of fame or a bulging wallet, but the bottom line is that we're all human, we all want to get laid, and there are ways and means of achieving it. These celebrity stud muffins show us how. The bastards.

Judging by what's written, these guys simply don't have barren patches – that's not in their vocabulary. Speaking of which, if you've ever struggled for new terms of reference for a girl's naughty bits, then struggle no more: 'balloon knot' and 'rusty sheriff's badge' are used to describe what I previously called the front bottom and the, erm, bottom. But hey, I'm just a dumb kid with a wet dream, not a bona fide celebrity drenched in such hot, rampant sex that everyday linguistic terms simply don't apply.

A few of you may find some of the content shocking. And fair enough – some of it is genuinely sordid stuff. One tale – the epitome of lad culture – involves the exchanging of high fives during a spit roast; another encounter ends with Mr M struggling to contain himself as he watches his latest conquest answer the phone to her boyfriend (and his best mate) with a mouthful of recently delivered semen. While these may be examples of extreme, explicit and morally dubious behaviour, are they not merely reflective of society as a whole? Let's face it, today a Christmas party piss-up at a Premiership football club is no longer an innocent meal out with the WAGS; it's a gaggle of hand-picked women and hotel suites hosting a series of drunken, drug-fuelled gang bangs. Allegedly.

'**The Seven Worst Men in London**' is our VIP ticket to that hotel suite. Dragging us past the wannabes, groupies and hangers-on, it takes us across the red carpet and, via a couple of white lines and a blow job from some star-fucker in the toilet, leads us into a cocked-up world of sleazy debauchery that would make Caligula blush.

But what lifts these stories above and beyond the realm of the purely pornographic is the honesty of those who have chosen to reveal their darkest, most filthy secrets. These are primal, raw, authentic tales of pure excess where famous names reveal what it's like to be given the opportunity to misbehave and to indulge their darkest carnal fantasies. And I wonder...given the opportunity, who wouldn't follow suit?

The truth is that, in the end, celebrities are no different to the rest of us civilians. Most of us are filthy animals just waiting for the chance to burst out of the closet that our moral compass chains us to.

In fact, I'd go further: my suspicion is that there is hardly anyone – celebrity or Joe Public – whose sex life, if it were broadcast, would not leave their family, friends and neighbours in a state of shock and awe. Oh my God! That's it! If Bush and Blair had just dumped loads of copies of this book in Iraq we could have spread world peace and democracy, and the Middle East crisis would have been solved!

Oh well.

Ashley Hames

Introduction by Giles Vickers Jones

It's not the most conventional subject matter or indeed an obvious bunch of stories that everyone will want to read. That said, it's something I and many others are hugely intrigued, compelled, inspired and, in a very male/laddish way, impressed by. Let me explain why I decided to put this book together. Over the last seven years, since graduating from university with a BA Hons in French and Business, I decided to make my own path as a TV presenter and along the way became a model, a writer, a columnist, a TV producer, a novice entrepreneur, and am currently a TV presenter and now an author. The whole journey has been full of stories. My whole existence beyond paying bills and obviously being a model citizen has been all about ticking boxes!

This is an expression I've coined with friends and in a nutshell it's about cramming as much into my life as I can. At the risk of sounding slightly lofty and pretentious, I want to make my own path in life and do things which are less than conventional, be it in my personal life, the way I conduct myself in my professional life, or in the experiences I undertake. I did have a graduate job lined up straight after university and had I taken that path my life would be a lot different, no doubt. But now, in my thirtieth year, I feel I've crammed more into my life than someone ten years my senior. I won't drag on about various personal boxes' ticking but let's say there isn't much that I haven't done, and the boxes I wanted to tick have now been achieved and more added!

The strange thing about a life which is less than mainstream is that you come into contact with a lot of very different people: the kind of people who you see in the papers or on the big screen. People who get celebrated for their sporting achievements and even some of their personal ones as well. Meeting celebrities becomes the norm as does befriending these people who you once thought were untouchable. The thing about celebrity is that it gives you a secret key. Let me explain: imagine you were to take a long hard look at yourself in the mirror, you know that time when your hair looks just right, your skin is glowing, your physique looks sharp, your clothes fit perfectly, and life just seems right. How does that make you feel? I can tell you that it makes you feel pretty invincible. You have confidence, you have bravado and this shines through and frankly makes you a lot more attractive to the opposite sex! Being famous gives you all that and most of the time not just that odd occasion when you get yourself dolled up. For celebrities, they feel like that when they go to the gym, when they head to the shops to buy a paper, or even visiting family and friends. The reason is they have validation because, strange as it may seem, your average folk are impressed that they have fame.

Obviously this is very transient and there is nothing to hold on to, but it does give the said celebrity that elevated sense of self-worth and appeal. Being famous is like marking your looks out of ten and then adding two more points as you are now instantly that bit more appealing. I've got celebrity friends from all walks of life as you would expect from someone who mixes their type of work and people they come into contact with. The thing I've noticed that does not change with fame is that if you are a prat you are still a prat, just a little better known. The problem with being famous is that some people don't feel they need to still be a good person as having that fame gives you a buffer.

Now I'm not a psychologist so that's my limited wisdom

on people and celebrity, except to say being famous does get you laid! It's not the holy grail of existence and the people I have in my book are famous, yes! But their success with women is down to their own abilities, down to their desire or drive for the opposite sex. I guess you know what this book is about: the seven worst men in London. I'm keen to point out that the reason these stories are being put into a book is these seven men are exactly what we think an alpha male should be when we were fourteen. Can you remember those schoolboy fantasies that you have when you watch the TV or a film and think one day I want to have whatever women I want and do all these outrageous things? Well, these seven guys have done everything and more. These are stories we've shared in pubs, in bars, on planes, on shoots. I've always been impressed by these seven men. I'm not condoning everything about them but they certainly squeeze everything out of life!

I've always enjoyed regaling these guys' stories, to friends who don't know them, to people I meet on random occasions and everyone's jaw drops in amazement. For that reason I suppose I wanted to retell these stories. We've got things that we cherish in a very sexually egotistical way but to have as many stories as these seven, and in abundance, is frankly phenomenal.

Over the last five years sex has no longer been seen as taboo and books and manuals about sex, about pick-up techniques and appealing to the opposite sex have saturated the market. Everyone has an opinion about how to pick up strangers, how to get a meaningful relationship, and, in some instances, how to become the ultimate pick-up artist. That's all fine and dandy and it's good to know there is help out there. But what if we walked alongside the very people who do it day in, day out without guides, without resorting to rip-off seminars preying on the lowly, the ones with no self-esteem and the hapless men who can't pick up women. These men are here today and really pick up women in the most primal way, perhaps as man was intended to.

I think one of the most boring subjects is people who drone on about their various successes in life, with money, with work. So this book has one very simple message and that is these seven men are the most successful men I know at picking up women, plain and simple! I have wanted to put this into a book for a long time and only through a chance meeting with an old friend did this come about. The reason I think this is interesting is because there is no ulterior motive to doing this book, the seven guys are all anonymous so it won't help their profiles; they aren't trying to make money by setting themselves up as sex gurus. They just want to share with you what their lives are sometimes fantastically like.

These seven men are the type of guys who could be drinking a coffee and then have the audacity to slip their number to the waitress serving them. I've actually seen one of them walk off with a friend's wife into the club toilets whilst his friend just sat in the bar. Let's just say when it comes to picking up women or dating, these guys are ruthless. They really are wrong 'uns but it is something to behold, and I guess I really think we all should know what is out there. Should you be the type of person who wants to pick up women, maybe you will learn something. Maybe you are already an artist when it comes to *amour*, then again maybe you aren't.

There is a chance that I could be considered a little chauvinistic for wanting to put this book out there, for bringing these stories to reality on the page. For that I implore that you read this with an open mind. It is a lifestyle choice to pick up women, a lifestyle choice to be so carefree and live in abandonment when it comes to sex. Everyone has their own boundaries and I suppose these seven don't when it comes to sex. I don't want to cause a scandal or make people appalled. To be honest, if people are then I challenge them to be perfect in other walks of life with their moral compass. It is just about me telling you folks about people I know, people you probably know and things that a lot just don't know exists beyond our imagination.

'**The Seven Worst Men in London**' is individual stories from seven men who love to be with women in as many situations, experiences and scenarios as possible before time runs out. These men are the real deal and I think they deserve to be written about in a book. As wrong as promiscuity is, it is also right and, let's be honest, we all love a little bit of sex now and then. I hope you all get something out of this, be it arousal, a freer mind, or just affirmation of what you are all about. The strange thing is that, as they are all anonymous, you won't know who the individuals are, but you will hopefully identify with why they do it. The reality is that it's a huge departure from the norm. The stories are all true and in their own words. All seven of the guys have met with me over the last six months and told me their stories. I've typed them up and retyped them and this, my friend, is the finished article: seven men all from London, seven stories all true and here for you.

Enjoy these seven men and their seven stories!

Racing Car Driver

This is one of those guys who everyone knows of or who has a story about a night out with him. He is a good-looking guy; as a racing car driver and ex-motocrosser you can imagine he is a little out there. I personally love the fact that he is such a nutcase. If I was to describe him, I'd say he is a menace, a deviant. He crams more into his life than ten people; every day he does something that surprises me. One of Mr F's main ambitions is to have as much fun as he can. There has never been a time that we've been out that he hasn't done something that makes people seem absurdly normal. So what is his technique with women? I honestly feel that people just think he is so crazy that they would describe him as a bad boy. I've never seen him not pick up a woman or two.

You would know who he is: in his heyday he won many racing championships on the British circuit and the international one. He has also dated a series of high-profile women with some very famous break-ups and a lot of column inches given to his womanising. He takes part in almost everything life throws at him and this extends to the ladies, but he is far more layered than just picking up girls. But this book is about the seven worst men and he is one of the very worst. Enjoy!

I have always been attracted to the natural beauty of a woman. I've always had strong physical attractions towards beautiful women, I've been lucky enough to meet some of the most stunning specimens across the planet!

I suppose it all started back in my schooldays when it was a bit of a challenge between friends to see who could bag the fittest bird, seal the deal and move onto the next project as soon as possible... I just never seem to have grown out of it! It's all about the chase and the challenge; the harder a girl plays to get, the more you want her but it also backfires on them as the harder they play the harder we drop 'em when we eventually get 'em! Girls play exactly the same game but are more ruthless with it.

I don't think people like me are bad people in the slightest! We're just spontaneous people who love fucking, and if you lay your cards on the table with a girl straightaway there is no harm done as they know exactly what they are getting into. Don't get me wrong here as I am a gentleman at the same time. To be honest, most girls out there a lot of the time just want a good fucking pounding, no strings attached and it's men like me that provide that service.

Sex, brasses, unsatisfied wives... it's just a hobby at the end of the day, let's be honest here. You're not going to settle down with a girl who sucks your cock in the first hour of meeting you, and demands you ram your penis up her arse on the first date. These girls are fun, yeah, and just what you want for a one-night stand, but if you want to give a girl a little run as maybe a regular, you want to work for this, chase for it, then fuck her arse and cum on her face... ha, ha…

I used to run a six-fuck rule... so I could never get too attached to a girl as I didn't have time for that in the racing world! After six that would be it: sorry, love, I can't see you any more, it's not going to work, and move on to the next conquest. That way they never get too hurt either as they have not had the time to fall for you that badly in six fucks!! Sometimes I don't even sleep with a girl. Once you know for certain you could if you wanted, that's the chase done and self-satisfaction complete, without getting involved in what could be a world of trouble. (Very rare though!) It's the girls that try to play hard to get that thrive my mojo!! The ones that show no interest whatsoever... the ones that make you work, where you have to pull out all your old tricks... it's like racing: it would be boring if the race was just laid on plate for you and you were guaranteed to win every one...

1 A quick check-up

When I first started to get known around town for my racing talent, the girls just started to flow in a little more easily and a little more frequently! One day I went into central London to meet a friend for lunch. I had an appointment at a new dentist in town around three o'clock for a check-up, so no booze was consumed on that day though, not that I'm an alky, I just love a good shant when I'm not racing. Anyway I had a good catch-up with my friend and exchanged some great sex stories. This particular friend is filth and I have shared many a lady with this man, but when we meet up it's almost like a competition of who has had the most action. Although I was doing well he seemed to have been doing a lot better, so I left this lunch on a bit of a downer to make my way to the dentist. Thinking, the fucker, he's cleaning up, maybe I'm not doing so well with the chicks here.

I arrive at the dentist around half an hour early. This is the flashiest dentist I have ever seen with a massively grand entrance. As I come through the entrance and into the reception area I'm greeted at the desk by a rather attractive blonde with a set of tits that look like they were just about to ping the button from her white dentist's uniform. She had a little pair of specs on that rested on the end of her nose, and was probably around twenty-three years old. I thought to myself, Jesus, that will do me any day. She's oozing with sex appeal, as I rest my arms on the desk and say, "Hi, I'm here for the three o'clock appointment." She lifts her head up from the paperwork she was doing and says, "Hi, I'm Julie, I will be the dental assistant for you today," at the same time giving the most flirty look I have ever received. She then drops in that she had seen me out in a club a few weeks back, and gives me a little wink. I'm loving the forwardness here and start to flirt heavily back. She says, "Give me a sec while I find your details." She turns around and squats down to a filing cabinet facing away from me where her pink thong rides up high in full view for me to gawp at. The arse was not ideal, I mean it was not overly big, just quite a bit more than a handful, but it looked firm so didn't put me off too much. Actually it didn't put me off whatsoever. I was just imagining myself pounding it as hard as I could, it was one of those, you know the type, where it's got enough firm meat to get a right bouncing rhythm going thrusting into it as hard as you can with no bone clash. As she turns round she drops the paperwork all over floor, scrapes it all together and says under her breath, "Sorry, I had a few too many glasses of wine at lunch" giving me another very cheeky wink.

I then go and sit in waiting area about two metres from where Julie is scuffling around with the papers. She keeps looking over every five seconds and giving me the look. I'm starting to feel a little on edge here, she's making it so obvious and there are another two or three other people in the waiting area. She then gets a phone call, picks it up to answer and spins the chair round to face me, spending the whole time on the phone staring at me, playing with her lips with her fingers (mouth lips, that is). I think nothing of it whatsoever, just thought she was bit tipsy from her lunch break! As she puts the phone down she says, "Right Mr ….., would you like to come through." I jump out of the chair and proceed to follow her down a long corridor towards the dentist's room at the end. But around halfway down she grabs my wrist, pulls me into the disabled toilet, and quietly shuts the door behind us. With that I'm saying, "What are you doing! Are you mad!" She raises her finger up to her lips and says, "Ssssshhhhhhhhhhhh. It's just a bit of fun." This is around half two on a Monday afternoon. I was not expecting anything like this to happen in the slightest.

She puts her arms around me and starts kissing my neck very gently. She's one of these girls who wears a smear too much make-up may I add, as her lips stick to my neck when she pulls away as she obviously has a whole bottle of gloss on. I wrap my arms round to grip her bouncy pert bum, and grab her cheeks with my hand and stick my tongue down her throat. She is an amazing kisser and this kiss probably lasts a whole minute without detaching lips. I'm thinking in my head if she kisses this good she must suck cock like a goddess, so I slowly start undoing my trousers so she will get the hint and go down on me. She stops kissing me and says, "I want to fuck you so bad but I have a boyfriend!" (So he wouldn't mind this, I think to myself? Girls of today, eh?)

I don't respond to this and she squats down revealing that pink thong again, but this time I have a bird's eye view! She pulls my cock out, gently wanking me off and licking my helmet too, then sucking me off real slow with an amazing twist grip rhythm. I was not wrong: she was amazing. She knows exactly what she's doing, and my legs are shaking with pleasure. This is very intense, a top three blowy I have ever had with ease!! I can feel myself about to come when she all of sudden stands up and looks me in the eye. (I'm thinking, oh, for fuck's sake right on the money shot she's going to stop and say sorry I can't do this, I have a boyfriend) but to my surprise she looks me in the eye and says, "Make sure you come in my mouth!!" Ha ha, I cannot believe it, and say, "With pleasure." I shoot and she swallows the lot. She opens the door, makes sure no one is coming and leads me to the dentist where she sits and assists him through the whole check-up. I leave with a wave goodbye and never see her again.

2 The perfect hour

It was probably around five years ago now, in my

home city, my friends and I used to hit the town every Thursday night religiously, for one reason only, to get nuts deep and compare stories over breakfast the next morning in our local café... (the poor waitress there overhearing our stories every week must have thought we were sex pest beasts from another planet!)

Anyway, this one particular Thursday me and the guys were on a mission. We started a few hours earlier than usual and swigged our way into town. By the time we hit the first club my testosterone was going through the roof. After ordering my first drink I thought to myself, I'm wasting no time at all tonight. As that thought left my head a cute skinny girl around 5'4 with the smallest skirt I had ever seen and the dirtiest little look on her face, probably about nineteen years old, walked over to me and said, "Hi, do you remember me? We had a brief chat a few weeks back." I replied with: "How could I forget a body like that!!" Anyway after exchanging about ten words of general chat I thought, fuck it and went in for the kill. Within seconds we're in deep tongue action slamming each other against the club's sweaty walls. I remember her nails so deep in my lower back I grabbed her throat till she eased them off...

After about six or seven minutes of this I grabbed her hand and said, "Follow me...." I was heading for the men's hoping that I could smuggle her into a cubicle. The gents was on the far side of the club and all the way over there she kept on saying, "I'm not going to fuck you tonight, I don't mind where you take me but I'm not going to have sex with you tonight. I'm not that sort of girl!"

I would say approximately two and half minutes later I'm sitting on the toilet with her facing towards me, tiny lace thong pulled to the side with her trusting my hard cock deep inside as if I was the last man on earth. I pulled her top down to reveal a massive set of perfect breasts that you would never match to her tiny frame but were one hundred per cent natural. Luckily there was no bog wog on duty that night, but we were getting cheers from outside from other guys as we were not holding back on the noise front in the slightest, and the cubicle was shaking so hard the walls almost fell down as I lifted her from my lap with her legs over my arms and with me standing up smashing her against the wall! (She was such a tiny little minx, barely weighing seven stone.) After around fifteen minutes and her coming twice I whispered in her ear, "I'm going to come any minute." With that she dropped to her knees, grabbed my weapon with both hands and swallowed the lot. As my vision came back I looked her deep in the one eye and thought, good girl, that's a proper bird!

With that a very angry bouncer knocked on the door vigorously shouting, "Right, you two, out!!!" As we got escorted out of the club she managed to vanish into the crowd to find her friends, avoiding being thrown out, whereas I was turfed out onto the street with a smile like a Cheshire cat!

As the night was still young, I started to make my way to another club. After walking along the seafront for about three minutes I see a small group of girls up ahead. As I pick up my pace and start to get closer I see this tall, slim, blonde, perfectly-shaped woman in a classy knee-length tight-fitting black dress and sexy six-inch black heels to match. Dying to see if she looks as outstanding from the front as she did from the back, I caught up so I was alongside them and to my surprise it was a girl I vaguely knew from out and about in London, who had been dating a very famous footballer for the last two years. After recognising each other, still walking, we paired off from her friends deep in very flirty conversation. All of a sudden she shouted over to her friends, "I'll meet you in the club, girls, I'm going for a quick drink with ……!!" I could see she had had her fair share of mojitos as I had pints, but I was like, fuck me, I think I'm in here!

But I was still thinking to myself, don't get your hopes up here. She is one fucking fine woman who looked a million dollars on this not so warm autumn evening! I thought I'm probably just about to get a bollocking for playing one of her mates or something.

Anyway, as we carry on walking, I'm mumbling on about some bollocks and she stops me in my path, and says, "Cut the crap, I want to fuck you right now!!" As you can imagine I almost fell over thinking is this my lucky night or I must have done one seriously good deed this week!

She then pulls me in close in front of a lot of people in the middle of the street (remember she is a very well-known wag in gossip magazines daily) licking my ears, whispering things you could only dream of. This woman was telling me she wanted me to fuck her now hard and fast. Then she said, "Right, let's go get a hotel right now." As I grab her hand (just like the other girl about half an hour before) to lead her to the nearest hotel, she digs her heel in, stops! I'm thinking, please don't say she has changed her mind! She pulls me in close, sticks her tongue down my throat for about twenty seconds then grabs my hand, starts walking towards the sea and says, "I want you to give me slow passionate sex on the beach." As we got close to the water's edge, I laid my coat down on the sand and she pushed me to the ground. This is one seriously demanding woman but I'm liking it a lot! She then proceeds to kneel down over me giving me a very slow dance placing my hands on her firm sculptured to perfection arse slowly raising her dress higher and higher.

At this point I'm so turned on as she unzips my trousers and runs her pert red lips down my throbbing cock groaning with delight. (I'm thinking, fucking lucky I shot my load in some other bird not so long ago or this would have been over before it started, if you know what I mean.) So before it's too late, I spin her over onto her back, slowly slip her black lace French knickers off, and proceed to plate her dripping wet stunningly groomed pussy until she starts vibrating into an intense orgasm. She then grabs my cock, inserts it inside her. I start to pump her with deep consistent rhythm until I come deep inside her.

After a little kiss and cuddle we dust ourselves off, swear to secrecy and go our separate ways into the night. At this point I'm chuffed to bits thinking no fucker is going to beat this story in the café tomorrow. After all, that's what this is all about! But at the same time I have just pumped two birds in the same hour bareback so a visit to the clinic might have to take priority over breakfast!

3 Funny island of lesbos

I know this isn't based in London but I've gone off the track as this is such a funny story and as I left from London there is a very miniscule link, but read it anyway!

It was my first ever trip to Amsterdam. A mixed group of about twenty of us headed over to 'the dam' for some drug-fuelled naughtiness. Pretty much ninety per cent of us had never been before so it was a very exciting trip, not knowing exactly what to expect. As we arrived at our hotel all the lads were straight onto the whore directory books left in the rooms for the guests, apart from the unlucky dumb motherfuckers that had brought their girlfriends with them. Everyone was getting a little too excited a little too early so we decided to head into the town to sample some local Jamaican woodbines and blow your socks off space shakes! Anyway this night was a definite write-off on the brass front, as we all ended up back at the hotel by 1am licking the walls too scared to go back outside in case the green monsters ate us.

So Day Two we set out to get pissed and smash our way round the red-light district. Around sevenish the drinks are flowing, when it gets out that one of the lads with us is only eighteen and still a virgin! So we looked at each other and thought, this boy needs some help. So we said, "Right, mate, you're coming with us!" As we walked through the red-light zone gaping at all the girls dancing in the windows we said to the boy, "Have a good look around, mate, and take your pick. We're paying for you to lose your virginity tonight!" With that he picked one fine specimen of an Eastern European girl and followed her down some stairs to her dungeon!

Shaking with jealousy and raging with horn my best friend and I looked at each other and said, "Right, let's get stuck in!!!" We had a good shop around to make sure we got an absolute beauty for our money. After all, that is the golden rule if you're paying for sex: she has to be front page magazine model standard!

We decided we would share our first one, for a good old-fashioned spit roast, as it's always a fucking good laugh shagging some brass to bits with your best mate (priceless fun)!!

So we dipped into a strip bar for one last drink before the search began for the lucky bitch that was just about to get sandwiched by two Brits on a rampage!! We agreed we were going to be patient and search for a dark-haired Jessica Alba lookalike slim curvy tanned girl, unlike our mates who all dived into the first girls they saw no matter what they looked like and blew all their cash on them.
So after a good half-hour search of seeing mostly mutant pigs and trannies we came across a street with some half decent candidates. By this point my mate was trying to dive into everyone he saw as they were such an improvement on the last three streets! I had to grab hold of him and say, "Whoa, whoa, hold up, there will be a princess amongst this lot, I'm telling you!"

Five minutes later there she is, standing about three steps up in a doorway leaning against the wall smoking a long thin cigarette. You could tell this girl had some serious attitude as she blew her smoke in two dribbling blokes' faces and raised the middle finger at them as if to say you could never afford me! As me and my friend approached, she turned her head and clocked us, luring us towards her with her finger, standing there with one hand on her hip, legs that could wrap around you twice, long brown wavy hair with a golden tan to die for, dressed in black silk stockings, suspenders, a lace push-up bra with like a long black see-through nightgown. She was stunning, her face was one of the prettiest I had ever seen. As we got there and introduced ourselves one guy was shouting, "Please, two hundred euros, that's all I have!" Her security took care of him as she invited us in. We explained we wanted to take her at the same time (even though I had fallen head over heels in love by this point and felt like bunging my mate and telling him to do one and shipping her back to the UK).

Anyway she agreed, but said it was going to be expensive and, fuck me, she was not wrong either. I think I gave about eight hundred euros upfront, but compared with the other girls averaging forty euros she was still worth it!

She sat us down in a little waiting area and said,

"You must wait here for half an hour" in a broken South American accent and as a couple walked past us into a room where it was just a curtain dividing the room between us and where she had done the business. After about five minutes she came back to the curtain and pulled it slightly open so we could see what was happening inside, and gave us a little wink! At this point we're like two little schoolkids peering through the gap in the curtain, and what we were about to witness was the most intense slow sexual live lesbian scenes you could ever dream of!!!

The girl's partner was out of our sight obviously wanking in the corner to his girlfriend getting seduced by one of the finest brasses on the planet!

After exactly half an hour the couple left, she cleaned herself up and called us through where she was rubbing her pussy through her see-through knickers on the bed in front of us! She offered us a beer, walked to the fridge to pull two ice-cold bottles of Becks out, bending over right in our faces giving us a face full of sweet pussy. We could almost smell it, it was that close. As she started to sway her hips around grinding to the background music, slowly taking off her bra she said to us, "You like cocaine?" to which we replied, "Yeah, we'll have a little line with you!" Over she came to the coffee table we were sat in front of, bent over again right in our faces where I could not resist giving her South American bum a little nibble at which she turned around and told us to take our clothes off. So in seconds my friend and I are side by side bollock naked! She then lifted a magazine to reveal three fuck off great lines like three fat slugs. She bent down yet again to hoover the whole line in one. I looked at my mate as if to say how the fuck am I going to fit that up my nostril!? Anyway we managed! And it was ROCKET FUEL! No exaggeration, our whole faces went numb instantly! As we approached the bed to get stuck into this goddess of a brass we both realised we had just made one big mistake!! The coke was so strong, both our throbbing cocks that had been rock solid for the last forty minutes after watching some serious girl on girl action had flopped massively. We knew we had to fight through this; we tried everything. At one point I'm trying to fold mine into her mouth whilst my pal is trying to fold his in her pussy, then vice versa! All credit due to the girl, she was trying every trick she knew. She kept stopping saying, "This not work, you too much coke." We were like, "No shit, Sherlock, you bloody fed it to us!!" And we refused to give up trying. It was a disaster, I even got my mate to hide around the corner just for five minutes in case we were putting each other off but it was no use. Once it's in your head that it ain't going to work you're fucked! It was the most frustrating situation I had ever had as this girl was absolutely stunning, pining to fuck us both, and the build was huge... we were like dogs on heat before the stupid fucking line! Then, just to top it off, about ten feet across this narrow street there was a window looking straight into ours where four blokes stood clutching beers doubled up in laughter absolutely crying their eyes out. They'd obviously watched the whole thing!

A BIG LESSON LEARNT THAT NIGHT!

4 Sisterly love

I had been seeing this girl for month or so. Nothing too serious. We had a good laugh, good sex and she had a cracking body with snide tits to die for that I still have a picture of to this day! Anyway she had a younger sister of about twenty-four or twenty-five. I had never met her, just knew she existed, and always wondered if she had qualities like her sis! A good friend of mine who was also top of his game in the motor sport world had met the girl I was seeing and was constantly badgering me to hook him up with the younger sis who was supposedly happy in a relationship.

A few weeks went by. It was a Tuesday night when Kelly the girl I was seeing calls me up to say, "Do you mind if my sis comes out with us tonight as she's had a bust-up with her fella and is feeling a bit down." I automatically said, "Yeah, of course, no problem." With my mate in mind, I then said to Kelly, "I'd better bring one of my mates out with us so she doesn't feel like a gooseberry!" Kelly said, "Yeah, cool, just as long as he doesn't get any funny ideas as she's still officially with her boyfriend."

So I call my dirty mate who had family plans that he dropped without the blink of an eye! To come meet the mysterious sister...

So we hit a few cocktail bars to start, and ended up getting a table in a swanky London club and started the champagne flowing. We're having a good crack and are all getting along like a house on fire. (Oh, I forgot to mention the sis was filth to look at; you could just tell: her look, her everything.) To tell the truth I was jealous of my mate because they were flirting heavily, and she was fresh meat to me. I'd fucked mine loads. I wanted the goddam little sis. I wasn't going to let this get the better of me so I focused my attention back on Kelly.

As the night went on, the sis and my mate went to the bar to get some more booze as our waitress was a dribble! Too slow to be a drip! Kelly then taps me on the shoulder and points towards the bar where they were standing. They were snogging each other's faces off. Now I'm really jealous, but thinking fair play to my mate as he was almost twice her age! This went on for a good ten minutes without detaching lips. It was quite a small club so they were not that far from us at all and it was pretty quiet so not much else was happening in there. Anyway Kelly suddenly says, "I'm done with watching them. Take me into the ladies and fuck me from behind." Now there's an offer a man can't refuse. She had never said anything like that before; maybe she sensed that her wee sis was giving me the horn and decided to up her game! So we sneaked into the ladies where she pulled her jeans down to her ankles, bent over and said, "Fuck me now," so I pulled my cock out which was already stonking just by what she had said to me, spat into my hand and gave her a fanny full of wet fingers ready for the entrance of my raging penis.

After returning to the table I suggested we go back to mine for a few drinks and a chill out (the four of us). We all agreed and made our way to the door. Obviously during the cab ride home my mate and I had all sorts of twisted pervy thoughts running through our minds! And by this point both sisters were in very high spirits too as we had been having a lot of fun. As we started to approach the entrance to my house, I had been kissing Kelly and my mate kissing the sis. The sis then pipes up and says, "Why don't we have a swap round and kiss each other's partners!!!??" Everyone thought this was a great idea until Kelly said, "I don't think so, it's not right, I'm not like that," which to be fair to her she wasn't... (boring bitch) ha...

So we go inside, crack open some wine, have a few lines of that... when sis pipes up again as she's looking out the window: "You didn't tell us you had an outside Jacuzzi!" I reply, "I was just getting to that bit, sweetheart... one problem is there is a strict no bathers rule out there." Within seconds she's naked. I turn around and so is Kelly. I look at my pal as if to say high-five, my friend, let's dive in. So I give the girls some robes and we all venture out to the Jacuzzi.

It was a perfectly clear cool evening with steam oozing from the hot water. We coupled off into separate corners of the tub canoodling away! As it was getting super-heated in my corner I peered over Kelly's shoulder to see the sis bent over the edge of the tub with my mate slipping in full length from behind. Within minutes I had Kelly in exactly the same position side by side, literally rubbing shoulders as we pump these two sisters from behind smiling at each other like we had just sealed a million-pound business deal! I then tapped my pal to say, "Watch this" as I slowly sucked my thumb, pulled Kelly's arse apart, spat on her coiner and rammed my thumb into her arsehole. With an almighty scream, Kelly looked back at me licking her lips, loving every moment. I then sucked my other thumb, lent across my mate and inserted it into her tight Gary Glitter! (So picture this, we're in the tub with both girls side by side leaning out the tub, bent over the side with my mate and I hanging out the back of these sisters, side by side in exactly the same position, with my left thumb in the girl's arse I'm fucking and my right thumb in the girl's arse my mate is fucking next to me).

FUCKING BRILLIANT SKILLS IF YOU ASK ME!

After this amazing Jacuzzi sex session we venture back inside to get some sleep. By this point my friend has to go back to his wife before he gets his bollocks cut off for being out too late. I show the sis to the spare room and slip into bed with Kelly where Round Two begins. She starts sucking my cock slowly and gracefully to get me hard again after our marathon tub session. Then she sits up and says, "I loved your thumb in my arse. I want you to fuck my arse slowly and finger my pussy from behind." This was great as we both watched each other in my full-length mirror next to my bed. I fucked her arse bareback until I came deep inside her butt pipe in time with her after me gently caressing her clit.

As we lay side by side slowly getting our breath back she slips off into a deep sleep. With that I'm thinking I'm never going to be able to sleep now knowing there is a horny as fuck younger sister alone in bed in my house. So I double-checked Kelly was asleep and made my way to the spare bedroom where the wee sis was lying awake. She looked me in the eye and said, "I've been hoping you would come in." She proceeds to suck my cock better than anyone I have ever met. In fact the sex was out of this world. It only lasted about thirty minutes but was mind-blowing. I managed to slip back into bed with Kelly and got away with it scot-free. Still to this day I wonder if they ever spoke about it.

Another successful night, and another two birds fucked bareback in the same night, with another early morning paranoid trip to the clinic!

I had a call from an old friend, saying that he had just bought and refurbished a trendy cocktail bar up North, and asking if I would make an appearance at his press launch night along with a bunch of other celebrities he had hired for the night. I had no plans for the evening so said, "Sure, I'll grab a couple of friends and fly up this evening. Be good to see you and catch up."

I knew this was going to be a good bash as this guy could throw a serious party. In fact what sold it for me on the phone was when he said, "Mate, it's going to be right up your street. It's going to be **seriously** female heavy!" So I rounded up the troops, some of my finest soldiers in fact, as I wanted to make a big dent in this party and nick all the women ourselves for a mass orgy in a hotel penthouse suite! (That was the game plan anyway.)

So four of us departed from Heathrow around 8pm to arrive at the location just as the party was getting heated. The lads ran off in all different directions like kids in a playground, so I had a chance to catch up with my old friend. As we chatted away, a very well-known glamour model, who was probably top of her game at this point in time and who I had nailed in the past, appeared through the crowd to say, "Hey you, what brings you up these parts? I haven't seen you in ages." Now this girl had something special: she could tell you exactly what she wanted to do to you just with her eyes, and on this particular night she was wearing virtually nothing. I must admit she did give the instant horn even though one of my rules is never back through closed doors unless it's the last resort and there is nothing else about. Always go for fresh!

She asked if I would like to join her and the girls on their table. I replied, "Yes, that would be nice. I'll round the boys up and come over shortly," knowing the boys would absolutely love to sit with these girls and graft away. So as I'm such a team player I called them over and we sat down and started chatting. There were about seven of these girls, all filth, playing up to the cameras, doing all they could to get recognised and be pictured in the next day's newspaper. Hey, whatever floats ya boat! As long as I'm not in these pictures, nothing is lost!

As the night went on there was some serious banter flying round the tables. With us boys pushing the limits and getting more and more cheeky as the night went on! As my friend's bar started to quieten down, the girls said they were about to move on to a local nightclub where they also had a table and asked us to join them once again.

So there we were, all piled in to one minicab en route to this club where there was all sorts of frolicking going down. It was great; the girls were snogging each other, licking each other, snogging us, licking us. Looking back it was one of the best cab rides of my life. Notice the way I say one of!! Maybe I'll tell you about one of my other taxi rides later!

So we arrive at this club, get ushered straight through to our table which is a big round table on a raised stage overlooking the whole main area of the club. As we all pile around this table and get our drinks sorted, a few of the girls get up and dance in front of the table. One of them is the sexy little fuck I mentioned earlier that came up to me in my mate's bar. Now she is dancing super sexy looking at me as if I was going to be in serious trouble if she got her hands on me. It was like the scene in Layer Cake where Sienna is dancing, eyeballing Daniel Craig. I'm getting very itchy feet at this point thinking, I'm going to have to go back through a set of closed doors here as I think I left some unfinished business behind! After necking her mate at the table which she didn't seem bothered about in the slightest, she came and sat next to me at the back of the table. As she starts talking to me she's rubbing my inner thigh and pressing her gorgeous firm breasts against my arm whilst kissing my neck in between words. Seconds later she starts to undo my jeans and slips her hand into my boxers, gently massaging my cock under the table. No one had a clue what was going on. I'm getting highly aroused here, then she bends down so her head is on my lap, pulls my dick out and begins to suck it (deep throat). Remember we've got people sitting either side of us and this table overlooks the whole club. But still no one has seemed to notice. She's down there a good three minutes and when she comes up for some air I lean forward to cover my huge erection, but she pushes me back and slides across to sit on my lap. She leans across the table to pour us both another drink as if everything is normal and nothing is going on. When the drinks are poured, she leans forward, pulls her thong to the side, grabs my cock in her left hand and slowly slides my hard-as-fuck dick into her hot dripping wet soft pussy. The smile on my face just grew ear to ear instantly!

The great thing is that, to anyone else watching, it just looked like she was sitting on my lap. Obviously a few peeps close like my mates were clued up we were up to something, but I was probably inside her a good half-hour still drinking and even had to exchange a few words with our friends when they came close to talk. Every now and then when no one was watching she would bounce up and down on my lap for a few seconds leaning back and groaning in my ear really working my penis! It was a great moment until I looked over her shoulder and saw a big angry bouncer wading his way through the crowd looking straight at us. I'm thinking, oh shit, busted big time, this could be real bad! So I tapped her frantically saying, "Quick, quick, get up, get off, security is coming." By the time she realised what was going on he had reached the table, leaned right across to us slamming his hands down on the table. With that, I curled up into the biggest cringe, super embarrassed, ready for a big bollocking, and to be humiliated in front the whole club, getting thrown out with my cock hanging out. Then he just leant across further and said, "Hi, I'm a big fan of yours, can I have your autograph?" I then leant back with the biggest sigh of relief with my cock still firmly inside her, turned to my pal who had just sat down next to us pointing to my lap, lip-reading, I'm fucking inside her whilst she talking to this fucking bouncer. He couldn't believe what he's seeing and just fell to pieces with laughter. Anyway she must have been talking to this bouncer for a good five minutes trying to get rid of him but still thrusting back and forth, pushing my cock deep inside her. My mate sitting across the table later told me he wondered why she kept going cross-eyed whilst talking to this door man.

It was a fucking funny yet scary experience. With a fucking horny twist, the doorman eventually left and I went on to come deep in her tight pussy.

Yet again… good fuckin girl! good fuckin night! good fuckin fuck!!!!!

6 Hard to stop

One sunny summer afternoon back in 2005, I had finished my day's chores by around 2pm and, as the sun was shinning, I had a right taste on for a few afternoon beers.

As most of my friends were still working at this point I was at a little bit of a loose end. I was just about to write the beers off and chill poolside when a friend called and said, "I'm in Covent Garden on my jacks. You around for a beer?" On that note, I leapt in the car and headed for Covent Garden.

As we all know, the sun pulls the women out from all sorts of places, so we were not short of skirt to look at. As the beers started to kick in and the early evening started to draw, we started to chat to a few ladies. As it was we ended up sitting with four very pretty but painfully well-to-do youngish girls. We had a good bit of banter going but at the same time respected the fact that they all seemed to be virgins and the subject of sex was all a bit giggly, so we played it very cool and kept the conversation light and decided to ease our way in gently, which seemed to work nicely as they invited us back to their balcony for some champagne and strawberries.

As we started to swig the champagne and up our game a bit to see if there was any chance of us getting our dicks wet with these posh chicks, it was around eleven o'clock when my friend slipped two magic blue pills into my hand and said, "Here, swallow these, then we have to get lucky!" I replied, "OK, if you want to play rock and roll I'm all for it, but two?" (These things were 100mg each, enough to give a donkey a hard-on for a week.) Anyway, down they went as we were pretty pissed by then and thought we were invincible!

So my pal goes back inside grafting his victim, whilst I stay on the balcony having a giggle with two little blonde numbers, getting hornier and hornier each second as the blue Vs start to kick in! My dick was getting hard every time she put the glass to her well glossed pouting lips! Then out pops my friend again who had just laid his cards down in a big way, and whispers to me, "We got to do one, mate, these birds hate me. I just put it on them and they freaked." I replied, "Mate, I'm doing alright out here. Where's your team spirit?" After a few seconds of heated discussion in the corner he says to me, "I'll take you somewhere special, I promise you I will not let you down." So I agreed and we left the cute stuck-up bitches that I had spent the last four hours slowly breaking down, with serious head rush and major throbbing cock syndrome. I looked at my mate and said, "This had better be good, you silly prick!"

He would not tell me exactly where we were going; he just kept saying, "Trust me, this is going to be good." So after around half an hour we arrive at this doorway in Soho. The doorman greets us and seems to be on first-name terms with my pal and shouts down to us as we're stumbling down the stairs, "You boys need any supplies?" I then scoot back up the stairs and grab two wraps of coke from the doorman in the hope that it will calm my throbbing cock down and make my legs a little more stable after the copious amounts of booze consumed.

As we reach the bottom of the staircase we seem to be in a very small but funky cocktail lounge, but the difference is there are around twenty to twenty-five gorgeous women from all different parts of the world strutting round in skimpy little outfits, taking turns in giving me the fuck-me look! I could not believe my eyes. We were obviously in a high-class hooker club. I had seen this a thousand times in other countries on much larger scales, but never in the UK! I didn't think they existed, to be honest. I thought the British hooker world just consisted of dingy little shit pit houses with skanky little over fucked Asians, so never bothered attending one.

This was far from that and I felt like I was in the riches of Spain. We were two of five guys in this place so the choice was pretty much ours from twenty-five sexy women. We had the raging horn and the stamina of two wild bulls thanks to the Viagra, pockets full of cash as things were pretty good for both of us, four hours of mental foreplay thanks to the posh tarts, and were buzzing our tits off thanks to the drugs and booze! This was perfect; we were as ready for this as Calzaghe was to give Jeff Lacy the spanking of his life! We were in perfect shape to start making our way through as many of these fine bitches as possible.

Now the way it works in this place is you chill at the bar, have a few drinks, chat with the girls, choose your victim, take them up to one of the rooms above, do your business, then come back down ready for the next. Well, that's our approach anyway! Most people come in for one, then flop off home! Within minutes my friend and I had both met some stunning Brazilian birds and taken them up to the rooms to kick off our marathon brass fest! I fell in love with mine as soon as her clothes came off. She gave me a short but sweet lap dance, then started to suck my cock very slowly, applying the Johnny using her mouth. She then got on top and rode me slowly but with serious rhythm. I then slid back up the headboard so her massive tanned tits were sitting perfectly in my face. This finished me off. To my embarrassment I came within about ten minutes of being in the room. I then went to the bathroom to clean myself up. Obviously still raging hard I go back into the room where the girl had put her clothes back on. "Errrr herrrrm," I said looking down at my piece, she looks me in the eye then down at my cock, looks all surprised and says, "You want more?" I reply, "Damn fucking right!" so I gave it to her once again, then came back down to the bar area where my friend was sitting with two different girls on his lap. One of the girls piped up in an Eastern European accent and said, "We've been waiting for you," followed by my mate saying, "Come on, mate, we're going to fuck these two together. It'll be a right laugh." So before I could even sit down I bashed a 'buca back and back upstairs ready for round 3 bird 2.

We went into a room that had a ten-man hot tub in the corner, mirrored floors, ceilings and walls, with a forty-inch plasma TV playing porn on the wall! I wish to this day I had this next hour on film as it was pure filth in every way!! I racked up some big fat lines for us and the girls and let the fun begin. This was and still is the most pornographic session of my life; it was wild!! We even invited a third girl up towards the end and some of the positions five people can actually get in is crazy.

After this we had a good forty-minute break at the bar laughing about the previous session and running our bar tab through the roof! We then went back to taking the girls up one at a time. As the night came to an end it stood that my pal had done six different girls and me seven. The funny thing was that I left the club around 9am with no cash, no phone, no chain around my neck, no watch and no cards. My friend was in the same situation but with no shirt either. This was because we had spunked all our cash and had to start pawning in goods for sex. The sex drive was unreal from 200mg of Viagra............!

Needless to say the friction burns on either side of my old boy put me out of the game for a good week!

7 The filthy hilarious shame

It was an E-fest trip in Ibiza around five years ago; I was out from racing with an injury. A few DJ friends of mine and I hit the white island for a long weekend and, as it stood, we ended up there for two weeks missing numerous flights.

One particularly messy morning we left a club in the beaming hot sun. The annoying thing was my two mates had picked up a couple of very doable chicks; one a little brunette French girl, very cute and super attractive accent, tiny little body to die for! My other friend was with a half good-looking, but in very good shape jack-ripper from Stringfellows in London who was also over on holiday. Big juicy tits. Long thin legs with even longer heels on, and hair down to her very toned ass. You know the drill: very slutty, but just what you need at 10am on the way back to hotel.

I was the wild gooseberry in front chewing my face off, obviously munched far too many pills for a girl to even look at me twice! I was more interested in the music pumping out from the clubs in the distance and chatting to every random Tom and Dick we walked past. You could say I was the entertainment for the night at my expense completely! The unlucky thing for my pal with the stripper was that he had to share a room with me, ha ha ha. As we came to the island at the last minute, it was the only available accommodation we could find, so when we got back to the room my other mate took his little

French bird to bed, and the three of us went into our room. We had two double beds pushed together. They started kissing and giggling next to me as I lay there staring at the ceiling with not a hope in hell of getting a hard on. I just wanted more Es!! Mind, this didn't last long. I started to get the horn eventually, the more they started to fumble with each other next to me.

I slipped off for a piss about fifteen minutes after being in the room. As I'm shaking the old boy off I can hear the moans and groans of the cute little French girl with my mate next door. This shot my mojo through the roof, literally!! I climbed on top of the toilet panel and gently and very quietly slid one of the roof panels across leaving me just enough room for me to climb into the rafters. I then very carefully made my way across the rafters until I was above their room. The groaning was the most beautiful sound I had ever heard. I just had to get a peek at this action! So then I lift another panel across, not even an inch, just enough for me to peek through. I got it perfectly: I was bang above the bed and she was sitting on top of him riding in true French style saying sexy French words in between groans, and they had no idea! Until I got a wee bit carried away and edged the gap to around four inches for a proper full view perv, (looking back at this, me sat in the roof of a hotel room perving over my mate shagging a frog cracks me up). Then all of a sudden my mate looks up towards the ceiling as he grunts with pleasure and clocks me looking down all wide-eyed with a big fat smile! Ha, that was one of the best facial expressions I had ever seen. The shock on his face was priceless. He's then frantically trying to tell me to fuck off under his breath in between pumps as the sexy Frenchy still has no idea I'm there. This then causes me to get a bad case of giggle fits. He was not happy but I could see he still found the funny side of it. So I closed the gap at his request and the Frenchy is none the wiser until I removed another panel completely and lowered myself down into the room right beside the bed in my pants, to her screaming with shock. I just strolled out the door as if nothing had happened.

I then get back into bed with the other two who had passed out by this point. I jump big in bed with them, with still no hope in hell of getting any sleep, so I try my chances with my mate's bit, the stripper. I keep slowly sliding my hand across and up her thigh to have my hand slapped and pushed away like a naughty schoolkid. I tried this a good seven times before I thought, fuck this, I'm off out to find a willing woman! So I freshen up in the bathroom, slip on some fresh clobber and make way to Bora Bora. I must have got eight steps down the corridor when I caught the eye of a maid I had seen a couple of days before, a Spanish chick who was giving me the heavy eye. She was cleaning one of the rooms along from mine. Now this chick ain't something you would do sober; come to think of it, you would need more than just booze too, but she was game in a big way and you could tell she would suck you dry with no questions asked. She had BIG tits with an arse to match, probably a good fifteen stone! But a pair of lips built for blow jobs, they were big juicy motherfuckers, and that was perfect in my situation, so as I approached the room she could tell I was as high as a kite as I was bouncing off the walls. She disappeared into the room, but when I got level with the room she was standing there giving me the finger to come in and licking her lips. I thought to myself, shall I? Shan't I? Then I thought, fuck it, dashed into the room, slammed the door behind me. She legged it towards me at which point I shat my pants. It was like she had not seen a bloke in ten years! She then slammed me against the back of the door, pinned my arms up and started necking the life out of me. It was barely legal what she did to me! She then frantically ripped my jeans open, popping the button off and busting the zip, and started wanking my cock so aggressively it hurt to be honest, but I was not going to argue with this beast of a woman. I then placed both my hands on top of her head and applied some heavy get-the-hint-bitch pressure downwards. She dropped to her knees and took my whole cock in straightaway deep throat, (remember I'm fucked up on Ecstasy here so this is just heaven beyond belief, the sensation was multiplied by a hundred). I then grabbed her hair either side and started skull-fucking this bitch hard, no holding back whatsoever. She was loving this and groaning a little too loud for my liking. It was more like a scream. I was thinking, fucking keep it down, you're going to get sacked in a minute. Anyway I was fucking her face hard and it was hitting the back of her throat hard with thick bile stringing from her mouth to my cock. I suddenly pulled out and shot all over her face. She was screaming with delight like some freak. I had not even touched her apart from her blow job handles. She started rubbing my cum around her face and tits then stood up, pushed me to one side and booted me out of the door shutting it behind me. I'm thinking, fuck me, I've just been raped by a room maid, and I fucking loved it!

Not a word was said between us! I was now standing in the hallway with my trousers round my ankles, shirt ripped open with cum all up my belly, messed up hair, red lipstick all over my face which was super red from the heat of what had just happened, when who popped out of the room down the corridor looking all fresh on her way home, but the cute fucking Frenchy! Doh! She strolled past, giving me the up and down look, shook her head and started laughing to herself as she left the hotel.

The Golfer

Without a doubt one of the funniest guys I've ever met, Mr B, has done everything with the fairer sex that you can imagine. We first met when I was on a trip to Spain and he was playing golf in a tournament over there. We met over a few beers, and from the get-go he regaled me with stories about his conquests, his friends' conquests, and even to the ladies he had met the night before. Unlike all the others, his technique is, I suppose, down to his mischief. He'll be the first to be on a table, the first to the bar, and the first to find any single girl in a room. Anyone who has ever met him will testify as to what a great guy he is, women and men alike. He is not sleazy, not a lecher, just very mischievous!

You would know who he is if you'd followed golf about four years ago. He was mixing it with some of the household names. A couple of times he made some big tours, but he is mostly known back here in the UK. He is a golf pro with a club in Surrey and still plays golf, but is setting up his own label now. He is the guy who wants to be everyone's friend. He is also a six-foot plus good-looking guy and has dabbled in modelling. When I asked if he would be interested in sharing some of his stories in the book, he was a little reluctant as he is a lot more settled now. Then again, he has enough stories to last ten lifetimes. Over to you, Mr B!

Since as long as I can remember I've had a way with the ladies. Maybe it's down to having a younger sister and wanting to demonstrate just how wrong men can be. Maybe it's down to the fact I've always been one of the boys and the ladies enjoy the fact that I'm a little sensitive underneath. Or maybe it's because I'm a good-looking bloke in great shape who plays golf for a living.

The thing is, I attract similar mates and they almost always have the same outlook on life which is the more we can cram in with the fairer sex the better our life will be. I'm sure at some point this may change, but for now I am almost certain this is why I do it. Life isn't coming twice!

Then again, the thing I always want to do is phone my mates the morning after the night before and share my stories… so maybe that's what it is: the stories with my mates. There is a whole bunch of reasons I'm better than anyone I know at attracting the ladies and really don't care what they think of me to a certain extent, so maybe the arrogance pays off. Who really knows. All I can say is I'm very good at picking up women!

1 West London bubbles

It started off as a very passive Wednesday evening in the suburb of London. Four young whippersnappers decided to venture out for an evening of debauchery. The usual misbehaving began with a little pub crawl checking out where all the best-looking ladies were; one drink and off to the next. In the end we settled on a place where you'd normally find an abundance of easy women. Being a Wednesday a lot of naughty girls venture out for mid-week fun. It began very slowly and after a few beers we decided to venture on to a local nightclub, a kind of spit and sawdust place but you've got to mix it up!

At first it was all pretty tame with the girls hanging around drinking their alco-pops, the usual goons hanging off them trying to chat them up, drinking their warm lager. Dotted around were little bits of wet stuff in the corner, nothing too exciting. Nothing really going on, so we carried on drinking a few shots to get our cocks ready. After not too long, up came a girl to my good self and asked, "How are you this evening?" We had a little chat but, to be honest, I fucking hate trying to chat in noisy clubs with the speakers banging over my shoulder. I was thinking let's cut out this chit-chat when, to my surprise, she asked me, "Are you looking for a bit of fun?" Of course I was looking for my own bit of fun which happened normally on a twice-weekly basis.

Anyway, she shot off like a catapult and came back with a plethora of mates. Let me describe them. There were three girls: one swamp donkey, a gorilla, and something that resembled, well, something that came out of my arse basically. My two buddies came over and we all began chatting for an hour or two. A kiss and a cuddle, nothing else happened beyond a sneaky little fiddle but just in case I took her number. We left, they left. We went and got a kebab. Probably the second bite into the kebab my phone goes and it's a text from this girl, Caroline I believe her name was. Now if you haven't pulled and you are on the way home thinking of missed opportunities and a message comes through like that, it makes you fucking happy. Guess all my legwork worked earlier!

The text goes 'What you guys up to later?' "Oh god," I said, "lads, it's half one in the morning. Can we really be bothered to go around to their house? Erm, yes we can! We are perverts!"

So a quick cab ride and we arrived at this massive house, a little nice for a twenty-year-old. She opened the door and, if I'm honest, I was still a little impressed at her balls for messaging us! Thinking I've got a feeling this could turn dirty, but needed her to say it, we said, "What's this all about?" She said, "This, gentlemen, is all about sex." Fucking lovely! We all piled through the door, went in and headed upstairs. We were led through into her dad's enormous bedroom. I'm thinking, please don't let father moose be here as my cockage is half mast. In the room the space was flanked by a couple of Egyptian mummies either side of us. Felt like being in a museum.

Finally we were led into a bathroom. It must have been the size of my whole flat: massive looking around, two showers, massive bowl sinks, this place was made for swapping bodily fluids. And there in the corner was an enormous bubbling hot tub surrounded by bottles of Laurent Perrier champagne. In the Jacuzzi were two of the birds that we had met earlier, fully naked, wet hair, with their huge fat breasts bouncing in the bath. Proper slappers, but looking a little better than the two heifers we met earlier in the evening. The one who met us fully lingeried up at the door was now stripped down revealing a surprisingly good physique and a tiny bush. She got in the Jacuzzi and said, "In you get, lads."

We couldn't believe it. So we stripped down stark bollock naked obviously, and got in. Straight away we paired off and I had the fit, well, fitter one all over my love muscle. It carried on until two of us were being noshed off by the others while the third was firmly planting it into the answerer of the door. Basically it became a free-for-all: birds were rubbing each other's clits, licking each other's nipples, whilst we watched and drank champagne. We had two on one, three on one whilst the others stroked their pussoirs, we had a full-on swap-around. Them with each other, me and my mate high-fiving over the fat bird, pouring champagne over their tits, you name it, we did it! Without a doubt, as dirty as we could possibly be with these girls in the master bedroom. Two hours later we got back in the car having scarpered sharpish and went on our way, severely over the limit but very satisfied.

2 The 4th emergency servicing

It was a Saturday a couple of years ago. Me and the boy went for a wander up the Brompton Road to meet up with a friend of ours in his local. We went in, sat down, had a couple of beers, just chilling enjoying the sunshine. I thought we'd get some gear in, made the phone call and the chop was in. Passed it around like Swiss cheese in the pub. Suddenly in walked a couple of, what seemed at the time after copious beers and gear, attractive young ladies. Let me describe them for you: one was 6 foot 1 clean-shaven with a moustache – joking! Anyway, these two lovely ladies lived together: one blonde, one brunette, probably 6/10 9/10 after seven or eight beers and a couple of lines that we'd had. Got chatting to one of them, the little blonde piece, not too bad, better of the two obviously. She was telling me she had been in a little distress all afternoon. She'd gone back to her little Renault 5 to find one of the naughty little chavs in the area had stuck a knife in her tyre and she had a puncture. A knight in shining armour, my good self, had arrived and she asked me to go back to her flat with her to change her tyre. I knew absolutely fuck all about changing tyres, let alone on a poxy Renault 5. The tyre was probably hidden under her boot along with all the other shit. I got back and there was one thing in my head and one thing in my head only and that was to give her an MOT! And I'm not on about servicing the car. So there we have it; strolling away from the pub I've got one thing on my fucking mind, my balls were like watermelons and the cock was hot and ready for action, ready for the service. I looked at the tyre and said, "I've got absolutely no clue and no chance of changing that tyre at all. Can't change that at all, love, but I'll have a cup of tea." We wandered inside, the tea turned into a glass of wine, to a cheeky line, to a bit of tongueing, to a little tickling of the scampi, the playing with the old cockerel. But before I reached the vanilla stroke I said it was time to go back to the pub; we couldn't leave the other boys out, including the gay boy.

We went back to the boozer. Everyone was there wondering why I didn't have oily hands. Little did they know I had brown hands but that wasn't from the car! The other boys had a sly wink across. Obviously they'd had a few more since then and a bit more of the dancing dust. The brunette looked over now and she could see I was keen on a bit of action. Anyway we drank up and went to our friend's flat not far away, maybe half a mile at the most. Got there and piled into this tiny little lift. I'm already sizing up the brunette as I've had a little go on the blonde one! She wasn't all that great so I left her with my mate. We've got into the flat, racked up a cheeky line and my gay mate got out some champagne, I believe. I put that to one side, shunned it and took the blonde number again into the bathroom and spotted loads of KY jelly, all sorts. I started tongueing and then slid my lubed finger straight up her balloon knot, licking the pussy, giving her the shocker finger up the arse, finger up the pussy! She is wanking me off, enough was enough, knickers down by her ankles, cock straight up the pussy, lovely silky little number, silky down to the wood like a wizard's sleeve, dripping, like a pork chop it was wet. Anyway, I'd had my fun with her, walked back into the lounge and I could see there was a twinkle in the dark-haired one's eye, something had to be done!

We left the gay boy in the flat, and me and my mate decided to take the two girls home. It was only right as it was some ungodly hour, about 2.30am. On the walk back I hadn't finished shooting all my conker water so I hung back with the dark-haired one. Having already laid down a few lines, she was very keen. My mate was walking ahead with the blonde. We were walking down an alley between Brompton Road and Fulham Road. Anyway I pushed her against the wall and swift as you like turned her around, pulled her knickers aside and stuck my cock in. I even remember standing in dog shit, but I thought, fuck it. All I could see twenty metres ahead was the bird I'd fucked an hour earlier walking with my mate. Anyway, I fucked her as hard and as fast as I could. It was hilarious, so I'm dragging her quickstep home sensing some serious action, got the serious horn. We all pile in through the door together, back into their flat, the scene of the crime earlier. All a bit of a blur, I remember trying to have a foursome but the two birds weren't really into it. Next thing I know, the blonde I was originally with has piled into bed with my mate, and me, I'm in bed with the brunette, and she's naked bar a pair of stilettos and is walking up and down my back in her heels, obviously some kinky thing she was into. I got the stilettos off and fucked her as hard as I could, spat on the arse, the rusty sheriff's badge, I could hear murmurings from next door, hilarious. Anyway, shot my glue, not interested anymore and managed to get an hour's sleep. I woke up and the brunette had gone to work, so she left me in her bedroom which also doubled as an office. I was kind of in and out of sleep. It was maybe 10am and someone was creeping in to turn on the computer. It was the blonde one who I'd first fucked ten hours ago and had been rafted by my mate all night! Oh yes, my fantasies from the night before had come true: the blonde one was sitting twiddling with her mouse, naked on the computer stool, so I called her over, and got her crouching on the cockerel, fucked her hard. Whilst still in the midst, in walked my mate fully clothed. Hilariously he said, "Hey, what's going on? That's my bird." He laughed and I shot my load, so I'd done the blonde twice, the brunette twice, then the blonde again! Slightly sore. The moral of this story is making sure you get your mechanics badge when in the scouts!

3 Cock pit encounter

It was late summer and I was due to go out to Hong Kong for a tournament. My bird was actually out there anyway working, so I hadn't had sex for a few weeks and was saving it for when I met up with her. So excited, got to the airport four hours early so I could check out all the airport talent, have a few beers and watch the world go by. But I had the serious horn as thirteen hours away was my girlfriend's pussy. I saw all sorts of beasts at the airport. I had the horn so much I even went into one of the toilet cubicles and knocked one off. I was desperate, desperate for it.

Anyway the ping-pong came around: flight to Hong Kong, gate now open, gate number 5, on we go! Eleven hours to go. I was so fucking excited. Sadly I was strapped for cash so turned right up the aisle and headed to cattle class. Sat right in the middle of a row of four, there were a couple of people to the right, but a space to my left. So I'm chuffed to bits thinking I can relax to

Hong Kong with a bit of space and think of my cock being sucked when I get off the plane! The gates are just about to shut and suddenly this bird comes strolling down the plane. She's probably two stone overweight which isn't such a bad thing as she probably carrying most of it in her breasts. She has a bit of a belly but not too bad. The main thing is the breasts stick out further than the belly – always a good start! Anyway she sat down next to me, I had a little look at her. I mean I'd only just blown the top of the bottle half an hour ago so wasn't really feeling that horny at the time. She was alright though, doable. I'd had a few beers at the airport which probably helped, and I gave her a cheeky little smile as she sat down.

So I started relaxing on the plane, but what stuck in my mind was how bloody hot it was. It was the end of the summer and she had black trousers on and a thong that was clearly chewing up her arse cheeks. She had fucking big tits and that's all I remember focusing on. My attention was just on those tits and as I got more and more turned on I kept thinking one way or another I'm having a toss over those tits if she is there or not! Captain comes on, seatbelts on and all that bollocks. Next thing you know we are in the air, and as you know rules and boundaries don't exist in the air. No airborne sheriff anyway. Anyway, about an hour into the flight along come the trolley dollies so I grab a couple of G and Ts and a couple of Heinekens. I noticed the girl next to me, who was South African, nineteen, been travelling, didn't have a boyfriend, not bad for just one hour's chat, had started drinking brandies. She was either a nervous flyer or thought I was an ugly cunt and thought she had a chance! There was some flirting and the stewardess was coming up and down, things were going well. By this time I had about nine hours until I was going to get my cock sucked. My missus was going to meet me at the airport. It was bloody handsome.

Anyway, the bird decided to kick back and watch a film, which kicked into touch the two hours' spade work I'd put in. Anyhow, I thought fuck this and put on the same film which turned out to be a little romantic number. About half an hour in I could see she was getting a little bit twitchy, lifting her bum up a bit in the seat clearly getting moist, damp, lovely! I could see the chance was getting closer; it was like a lion chasing down a gazelle in the cape flats of South Africa! Anyhow the film was drawing to a close and there was a sexual scene at the end. I can't remember exactly what the scene was but it caused her to look slightly in my direction. Fuck me, I got a rock on half a bar straightaway, hard as a miner. If I was going to do this, now was my chance. I did a well-known little trick: I put my finger very calmly on the edge of her thigh. So if I got the wrong reaction I could say, "Oh sorry, love, accident, pure chance, complete mistake." But she turned and let it linger a little bit. She didn't flinch, so I put a couple of extra fingers on her thigh so it was more deliberate. I was seriously taking a chance here, but as I put more pressure on her thigh she faced me a little and gave me a smile. Bang, that was it! I was going to seal the deal! She then moved her hand onto my hand and slid it more central towards her upper thigh.

Christ, I thought, this isn't happening to me. I'm meeting my bird in Hong Kong. I've got seven hours left. I haven't had a shag in a good few weeks and only had a wank a few hours earlier. Which felt like a lifetime and I've got a bird with big tits and not a bad little arse. I was getting excited, things were going through my head. Fuck it, I took the plunge. I took her hand off mine and pushed my hand straight up to her pussy. I could feel it was a hairy pussy even through those black trousers. But I wasn't bothered, I would have stuck it in a rabbit hole, I was that horny! Slowly got her hand and moved it to my cock, and blood was pumping through it like I was on a life support machine. It was unbelievable, things were going to go off and if it wasn't going to be my cock in the next five minutes, something had to happen! So I rubbed the old pussy for a bit and my fingers were getting wet through the fabric. I had a little sniff and it smelt alright. I went down inside; God, I was right: it was a hairy old beast but I couldn't have given a fuck at the time. She started getting the cock out pulling the blanket over us. She was tugging it, wanking it, spitting on it, she was treating it like a compass, shoving it in every direction bar the right one! I slipped my hand up her top and to my sheer delight I felt right massive big kahunas bullet nipples! I was in my element and I had to try and get this bird to the toilet as quick as I could without shooting the glue.

The lights were dimmed as everyone was trying to go to sleep. The meal had been served. I was fucking raging, this bird was mine, she was wanking me like a mentalist, I was fingering her pussy under her thong, it's so wet and I'm about to go off here. Right, I didn't say anything; in fact I didn't even know her name. Not fucking interested. Anyway I grabbed her hand and led her to the toilets. The toilets were literally five paces away, so we got in the toilets and fumbled getting her big old farter in there. We shut the door, I pulled down her tight black trousers, pulled down her knickers and I've just got her pussy dripping at me. I've whipped down my trousers and just fucked it as hard as I've ever fucked anything in my life. I must have lasted a good thirty seconds, maybe thirty-five! I've never told anyone this but I shot my glue straight up her, so I could well have a little springbok somewhere. Fucking messy.

So I did my flies up, let her wipe herself up, went back to the seat, didn't talk to her, didn't kiss her, didn't cuddle her, fell asleep, woke up, didn't look at her. Got off the plane and made a sharp dash for the way out to meet my girlfriend, couldn't wait for sex on the way back to the hotel. I fucked her in the car on the way back, I didn't even wash my cock. Now I'll tell you a secret: the bird on the plane was ginger and a little whiffy, but fuck it. Fucked my bird, came all over her face, dried my cock, drove back to her apartment, end of! Just a standard flight for me.

4 Like mother like daughter

This is going back a few years, and involves a bird I'd met at university actually. She was a little honey and, I'd say, tidy. Nothing massively to write home about but you could tell she was from good stock. Liked naughty underwear, dressed nicely, spoke well, quite into her fitness. She was an above average bird, I suppose. Now I'd never met her mum and dad before, and she took me home to meet them in Shropshire one weekend. Slightly nervous we get to the door and her dad answers. He seems like a nice guy, friendly. Whilst there I clocked her mum's behind, and she looked alright, maybe better looking than the daughter! I was at that kind of age where I quite fancied the older woman. She was an older model anyways and I just thought I want that, that is fucking lovely.

The weekend came and went, nothing spectacular to talk about. We went out for a few meals, had some drinks, bit of TV, the usual, nothing crazy. Sex with the daughter. Anyway I've gone back to university and a month later the mum and dad have come to visit our student house, everyone is out. We've had a few drinks, some Chinese, everyone is pretty battered, the dad had passed out in the armchair, and the daughter, my girlfriend, is asleep next to me. I'm getting fucking excited. In fact, let me let you into a little secret here. I was hoping that something might happen. Earlier on I'd had some mental signals from the mum and I was thinking she fancied me. So I took the lining out of one part of the pocket in my jeans. Underneath I was completely commando. The room is asleep bar the mum and me who are both watching TV. Now this is a daring move, and I am really going to be in some trouble if this backfires, not least from her husband who is sitting six feet away. Let alone my bird going ballistic.

So I looked across at the mum who looks great in

the flickering light. She isn't really paying attention but I'm certain I've sized her up. Even the month before when I met her she had that way: she held your gaze too long, quite tactile. I could tell she was dirty. Anyway they were both asleep, so I put my hand behind the sofa and across to her and tickled the back of her head, and she looked over and sort of smiled a bit. I just thought, oh my God, what am I doing? This is my girlfriend's mum, so wrong, but this is so right. This is going to get me dick points for the rest of time. Anyway she did smile but I couldn't quite work out what it meant. Did it mean, "Oi, you prick, back off that's my daughter next to you!" or was it a "What you going to do?" She was nervously checking if her husband or daughter were awake which they weren't.

So I took the plunge. I took her hand. I still can't believe I'm doing this. So I've put her hand into my pocket and straight onto my cock which was fully erect and she started playing with my cock, wanking it a bit when all of a sudden the phone rings, everyone kind of wakes up and she whips her hand out quick as you like. It was the biggest anticlimax I'd ever had. Anyway I took the daughter upstairs and fucked her all night just imagining it was the mum I was fucking. Her mum had a massive effect on me. So the night passed and in the morning I've come down, and as luck would have it the daughter has gone to lectures and her dad had to go and sort something out with the car, which just left me and her mum alone in the house. As I walked down her mum was sitting in a dressing gown in the lounge. I actually thought this must be a wind-up. I'm speechless now as I was then. She was in her daughter's dressing gown, still with bed hair but looking bloody lovely, a yummy mummy, whatever you want to call it, she was. There were so many thoughts going through my head as I sat down not really even mentioning last night. I didn't know what to do, I was so excited.

She got up and went to the kitchen, asking if I wanted a cup of tea. I said yes, knowing in my head of course I want a cup of tea and I want to spend as much time in your company as I possibly can! Because ultimately I want to lick your box. She gave me the tea and as I took the cup I slid my hand down on to hers which is pretty much a common trait for me. She looked up at me and I thought, fuck it, now or never. So I put down the tea and started tongueing her. She's not pulled away, this is it, this is it. I've pulled my boxers down and she is sucking the cock like you would not believe, licking it, it's lovely. I've undone her daughter's, my girlfriend's, dressing gown, and she's got pretty much an old pair of mummy apple catchers on, which I must admit did temporarily put a bit of a drag on the old hard-on. I whipped them off, and fucking hell she had a nice pussy considering she was forty-five! Without further ado I've just whacked it right up there and, I'm not kidding you, it is fucking awesome. I'm thinking of the dad and daughter coming back as I'm fucking her while she is sitting on the kitchen side. She is screaming and I'm thinking this is the rudest thing I've ever done in my life. I'm actually getting a rock on as I'm writing this. At the time I was so horny, she had rank tits so I don't go there, but I'm tongueing her, got my finger up her hoop, she's got it up mine. Anyways there is no way I'm spunking up my bird's box, so I pull out, turn her around and jizz all over her arse.

She calmly did up her dressing gown, put her

apple catchers back on, I put my boxers back on, had my cup of tea and just walked back upstairs, said nothing to her on the way up, had a shower and chilled out. My girlfriend came back three hours later. All the while I was in the room slightly awkward, slightly proud, slightly embarrassed, thinking what the hell have I just done. They headed off a couple of hours later that afternoon. Two weeks later my bird and I split up. I mean we were going nowhere and, to be honest, I couldn't face seeing her mum again. It would mean divorce, heartache, whatever if anyone found out! I must say though, if you ever get the chance, anyone, to do that, I promise that sexual buzz will not be beat!

5 Local lovelies

It was our winter, their summer in Cape Town. I had flown in for a couple of months' work and hopefully to bag myself a few saffers. Me and me bird had hired a place together just off the main drag, a tidy pad but fucking pricey, considering how cheap everything else is in Cape Town, but it would be worth it if only for a great shag palace. In true SA style when you have pounds to spend you may as well take advantage: chandeliers, great lighting, big TV and, more importantly, it had a killer hot tub.

Things had been a bit dodgy between me and the missus for a while as tales of my infidelity were starting to loom. She was always suspicious but it had been difficult plus I still felt like I needed to get a lot of pussy at the time. As I was travelling so much there were just too many temptations. Now let me just clear one of those up for you. The missus was out of town on a two-day job, which meant I had the place to myself and, more importantly, time to hit the town! So a mate had flown in for the weekend to partake in the frivolity.

He arrived in Cape Town and did his customary drug deal, couple of grams and then we were ready to roll. We started off down in Camps Bay in one of those wanky bars up top, full of prick teasers, the kind of place where wannabees would hang out, the drinks were overpriced and the clientele were not overly deep, but there were always birds to be had there. We had a quick line of chop and were off to the more local haunts.

Only a short walk away we stumbled across a decent outdoor bar fucking teeming with local snatch. We played the usual cat and mouse for an hour or so in between lines, then finally we spotted a couple of real potentials. One was a fit black girl and the other a tidy redhead. Not having had a black girl or a redhead before I was mega-keen.

After ten minutes of pure chat they were eating out of our hands, couple of drinks, once around the dance floor, then off back to the house. The dark girl seemed to take a liking to me. As we walked home I took a step back; she had the tightest arse and lovely plump tits. She was stunning, quite good chat but you could tell she was dirty. We arrived back and I could tell my buddy was gutted as he fancied the black girl. Don't worry, I told him, he could still get his wish, as I was thinking more and more of some devilish plan. I was like a fiend with the thoughts going through my mind.

We went out on to the balcony. He began chopping again and luckily the girls were also up for the sniff. High as fuck, I had to get this started, some lame conversation, a bit of music, and I shuffled the black girl onto my lap. I felt as I moved her she was going commando, lovely, I got half a bar on straightaway and, as if by magic, it triggered her into life. She could sense I was horny and I started necking it. My mate was still talking shop to the ginger but I could not give a fuck. I wanted the black pussy.

I stood up and walked her into my en suite, pulled down the mini dress and stuck my licker straight up her tiny arse. It tasted sweet as fuck, I put her hand on my cock and she grabbed on. By now I had moved on to the pussy, a silky number, I could not wait to fuck it. Wrapped up in the moment I forgot about my mate and his girl. Then I felt a presence as all this was going on and my instincts were true. Behind us stood watching were my pal and Charlie Dimmock. Fuck, that gave me the horn. I instructed him to manipulate her into the same position as mine. He could not get her skirt off quick enough. I had begun pumping again and the choir was singing at the top of its voice. Casually I tapped the boy on his arm and gave him the universal lads' sign for swap, so bang, we did. He was so keen to pump the black, no questions were asked and I just thought I could tick two boxes. Slightly ballsy, but often if you are in this situation, swapping is as easy as ordering a beer!

The ginger's fanny was tighter and, sorry lads, but I was soon at the vinegar stroke and as if in unison my pal was off like a bottle of bass next to me. Now these were not the sort of birds you wanted to hang around so I basically told them to get their knickers on and fuck off.

As I shut the door I saw a light on opposite me in the window with a face looking back. I thought no more of it and we racked up and laughed about what had just gone on. The next night I drove my pal back to the airport, proud as punch, I thought, another conquest closed, another story for my pump book, until on my way back from the airport my bird phoned. She wasn't meant to be calling then which meant something wasn't right. As she shouted down the phone the penny dropped. That face at the window was of course where her friend and her mum were staying. Shit! I managed to explain that I just passed out, all the usual bollocks. That I was only chatting with them and that I wasn't doing anything. Somehow I pulled that off, I'd become an expert through the years!

Anyhow, she eventually did find out and decided to pay me back by writing off my hire car before flying home and leaving the bill. All for a bit of ginger and black pussy, hilarious.

6 Vintage fun

I was out with some friends on a mid-week session, couple of model mates, good lads, boys about town up for a bit of a booze-up and shenanigans. We had a couple in a little boozer I know to clear the cobwebs followed by a few shots and we were on our way. One of the guys suggested a party around the corner. A mate of his was an actress and she had loads of sorts tagging along who might be up for a bit of how's your father when it came to closing time. The great thing is, he said, free booze and a table in a club in the West End.

I didn't need to be asked twice. We downed our drinks, quick hop in the cab and we are saying hello to all these ladies. True to his word there were some hotties in the club, and the bird was in a famous soap at the time so all the usual hangers-on. I didn't care as I was going to get my nuts wet even if it meant getting hold of a nice price bird at King's Cross. So the usual pleasantries are exchanged, a very random bunch of people: this older bird, must have been in her fifties who was her celebrity hairdresser, there was her producer, her agent and two or three friends including this really tasty blonde. Lovely little tits and you could tell she was up for it from the beginning. She was a little wild in the aisle, by then a bit tipsy and gave me a kiss instead of shaking my hand, result. So we all pile into the booze and I'm chatting up this bit of skirt, making some serious headway, am loving the free booze and feeling like a king, twenty-four years old, fit birds, celebrity, I've arrived.

It's all a bit of a blur towards the end, but what I do remember is piling into a cab and kissing this bird in the back on a long journey to what felt like Dover! I awoke in the morning with the usual stinking hangover and that dread. What the hell happened? As I searched the room, this all felt too grown-up, plush furniture, expensive furnishings, who the hell have I gone home with?! I looked towards the end of the bed and noticed a wig sat on a mannequin's head. Now, as a rule, I don't like too much hair, but this was a little Elton John. Sure enough to my left was a lady, phew, it wasn't the fit young thing. Things really had gone wrong: it was the celebrity hairdresser, all fifty-nine years of her.

I lay there with flashbacks going through my mind, remembering going down on her, remembering she likes it dry downstairs so she could feel it, yes she needed extra friction! I remember kissing her everything. It's 8.30am, I'm miles from home, shit. Making the usual bollocks excuses I jump up, head under tap, fully clothed and desperate to get the fuck out of Dodge. Now don't get me wrong; I appreciated the bed, and the new story for the boys, but I really wanted to get out of there sharpish.

She offers me to head down and make a cup of tea, and these are the worst bits; as the alcohol wears off, your self-loathing kicks in, so I'm downstairs when who walks in, her son! This is one of the worst moments ever. He stares at me, I mean he is seven years older and he must be thinking who the hell is this. The worst thing is his dad is on business, his mum has just sucked my cock and now I'm face to face with the knowledge that his mum doesn't know he is here. The whole thing is shameful, really wrong. To make things just a little more awkward, the builders turn up, the postie pops by, the son's wife is there and me sweating like a rapist in a coma unit whilst these six people stare at me like I'd fucked the woman upstairs, which obviously I had.

Whilst the flashes kept coming thick and fast I just couldn't believe I'd found myself in this position. As I slowly downed my tea she finally walked downstairs. She had a new hairpiece on and, to be fair, looked half decent. But all I could think is that this is the wrongest evening ever. She is fifty-nine, I'm twenty-four, she is married, she is my mate's celeb hairdresser, her son is sat opposite me and, to add to it, she is completely bald and I'm half an hour from home. Mortifying, but, fuck, what a funny night.

7 What a game bird

This story is funny as hell as it was one of my first ever sexual experiences with a mate. I'd only just broken through in golf so was in my early twenties, I suppose. It was during a break in training; I managed a night out with a mate who was in the army. Now it was one of my first times out in London so like most amateurs I made the mistake of heading to Leicester Square. That said, there was not a chance I wouldn't find a bird to have a horizontal shuffle with. So after a few sherberts in some of the tackiest bars ever we were feeling somewhat likely with ourselves.

It was about half ten and we found ourselves necking vodka shots and in a packed club and proceeded to terrorise the women. But that night really wasn't my night: I kept tonguing all the birds but most of them lived with their mum and dad and I wasn't forking out for a hotel. The night was dragging on and it started to become that witching hour, you know the time when the club is starting to empty bar the hardcore drinkers of the ugly lasses. So in the timeless tradition I did laps prowling for birds. My mate was nowhere to be seen at this point and, thinking he may have gone home, I was seriously upping the ante with bird hunting. Just doing laps of the club I felt like Ayrton Senna!

On my third lap and seriously looking like a wrong un I stumbled across my army mate practically making love to this bird; he was almost raping her with his hand. So I sat there like a proper lemon just waiting for someone to come past when the lights suddenly came on. Now this wasn't what I'd bargained for on my night out. As we are all stumbling out of the club it's starting to dawn on me: where the hell am I gonna stay as I'm with my mate in a hotel. Having just moved back into the country after a training camp I was in need of a bed. After a little bit of banter she invited us both back to her flat in East London. After what felt like an hour's walk we found ourselves at the bottom of a high-rise council flat. It turned out she lived alone even though she was only eighteen. We went through the door and, if I'm honest, it all felt a little depressing.

The lounge was fairly empty, it smelt a little of cat

pee, but bless her she was doing all she could to improve her life, I suppose. So she very kindly offers me her couch. So me and the cat settle to begin what was going to be probably my worst night's sleep being poked and prodded by the moggy cat. About half an hour into my sleep my mate comes through with a bouncing hard-on. Come on, quick get into her bed, she's in the bathroom fully naked. Now I'm no expert on modern law but isn't it illegal to be naked in some stranger's bed when she is least expecting it?!! Well, taking my chance I say goodbye to Whiskers and dart to the den of hopeful iniquity. The funniest sight: we are both in the bed naked my mate with a raging one-eyed monster and me nursing an ambitious one-eyed monster.

Then in she comes. She looks down and sees us both in the bed. She asks what I'm doing there and my mate manages to convince her it's alright. Meanwhile I'm checking out this proper little hottie, a little too much hair on the crease, but what a set of breasts, full milky and with a pale body catching in the moonlight I've completely forgotten about the cat piss in the air! Meanwhile she gets into bed between us and the fun is now beginning. He starts to kiss her while I lick her nipples. Basically I'm playing it cool so she doesn't bolt. Even in my infancy of sexual adventure I know it's all about making the girl feel safe at every opportunity! So with that I just took my time and licked her juicy nipples. Meanwhile my mate had moved south and was licking her love box, while I started kissing her. I couldn't believe it; here we are on a random night out and are both about to have our first threesome. As excitement goes it was properly exciting. So I decided to try my luck and pushed her hand to my cockerel and sure enough away she went, just thumping it for dear life. So I decided to try my luck a little more and go for the blowy and when she just took it down like a pro I knew we had a dirt bag.

Meanwhile my mate's licking her out for dear life. He even has three fingers up her balloon knot! After a while he puts it in and starts fucking the arse off her while I'm now skull fucking her. Like any good threesome nothing is complete unless you can both be inside her at the same time. Sure enough, and bearing in mind she is only eighteen years old, she suddenly says, "I want you both inside me at the same time."

I couldn't believe this; this seemingly innocent eighteen-year-old is about to have two grown men inside her at the same time. Suddenly I'm on my back, she is on my cock and my mate is being lubed up by her and guided up her arse. I kid you not, we must have rode the arse off it for almost half an hour. She was like a mad woman scratching us, pulling us into her, just begging us to fuck her more and more. We did the standard high fiving, but the pièce de résistance was a spot of bukkake. Now, never having done this before, we both knelt over her and it felt like we were in a porn film together. One of the funniest sights, us both wanking in perfect harmony with this complete stranger waiting below for our conker champagne. Then, quick as a flash, we've all emptied our pouches. I went back to the couch and he stayed in the bed. I couldn't stop smiling as I'd had that rite of passage and had a threesome with one of my best nights. Although I had flea bites and slept at most twenty minutes, that walk of shame was the best I'd ever had!

The Writer

This guy is someone I have known through the years. As he is a journalist you end up spending a lot of time meeting him at parties throughout London. He has dated his fair share of celebrities and is quite a respected writer and broadcaster. Whenever I've met up with Mr M he has a few women around him and is brazenly chatting them up. It's like he doesn't care what people think about him. Even though you might think he would be arrogant he is far from it. I suppose just confident is the best way to describe him. When I asked him what his technique is, he said it's just that he doesn't mind being knocked back as for him it just hardens the chase.

You'd know his writing: he has written two books, one about celebrity, and he has his own column and has contributed to all the major TV channels in the UK. A bit of a celebrity in his circles, he'll often be found at the back of the celeb magazines at those showbiz parties. I suppose he is Mr Showbiz. He has friends who are musicians, politicians, TV personalities and movie stars. He mixes with them all, but loves his women. This is his account of why he likes the ladies.

I don't know why I always feel this urge to be with women…it's a strange thing: every time I see a woman, and I mean every woman, I look at her and find something attractive: her face, her legs, her boobs, the way she dresses, is she flirty. Almost the minute I meet a woman I try and find as many ways as possible to connect, to find a way in. I'm a good-looking guy who has a lot of confidence, but I'm not arrogant, and the key that works for me is to make the girl laugh whilst putting yourself down, listening whilst making connections wherever you can. For me the thing that always works is to be confident; if you don't care if you fail but make every effort to impress, the success rate will lift.

Once I've got a woman on side, I become very cheeky, never sleazy and never make her feel uncomfortable. You'd be amazed at the amount of women I watch being chatted up and I can instantly tell when they lose interest. It is a game, one I'm very good at. I don't know why I have this desire because in all honesty I'm probably one of the kindest guys to women and hate to think they feel used, but that chase the minute they pull down their knickers, when you know you are in! And frankly the story you have to tell after!

Things occasionally slow down but then you meet someone new, or you are in a strange place and something strikes a chord and suddenly I'm back in the saddle. I've lost track of the number of women I've slept with. There are a few things still left to do and maybe one day I'll write a how-to book. But for now though it's just about the chase!

I guess it goes back to that Ollie Reed quote: 'I have two ambitions in life: one is to drink every pub dry, the other is to sleep with every woman on earth.'

1 More the merrier

A few weeks previous I'd been in this gay club in Soho; it's the kind of place where you can pick up women; rightly or wrongly it's a great haunt. The women let their guards down and it's a very open place to take drugs should you want to. That's probably down to the number of celebs that are always there. Anyway I was in there walking to the bar when this girl stops me and recognises me from a show I'd just been in. She's tipsy and clearly very up for a good time. The thing is she isn't really good-looking and if you're that drunk you kind of lose the horn somewhat. Not really thinking I fancy her but figuring I had nothing to lose, I said arrogantly, "Do you want to have sex?" She said yes there and then. Which was a bit of a shock to get such a quick reaction. I was with my mate at the time, so I said, "Only if you screw him too, a three-way." Once again without any hesitation she said yes!! So I went and got my mate who sadly had lost the battle with vodka. I went over to the girl, explained the predicament and that I had to take him home and said I'd take a rain check!! The thing is she wasn't amazing looking, but she had alright tits and face and seemed a bit slutty!

Anyhow a text came through a couple of days later saying, 'When are you and your mate going to show me a good time?' So we organised for a Tuesday after her work. I arranged for 6.30 so we could meet when it was still early enough to dip out if she was a rotter or if she got cold feet and we could head on elsewhere. The problem was on this particular day my mate couldn't make it, so I got another pal, who's a proper deviant and always up for a good time. As my first mate bailed so late I only had a couple of hours; he didn't need much persuading. He said yep and with only two hours' notice he met me and we waited for her in the bar. The bugger who was my other mate then agreed to do it and having asked both it seemed wrong to say no to either. Cue to two of us sat with her and my mate walks in so three men, one girl. It was already slightly strained; you know, that moment when you've met a girl and the conversation isn't really flowing so you work really hard to ask about them, their lives, their pets, whatever to keep the conversation flowing while the booze kicks in! Well, this was like that; me and my mate had nothing whatsoever in common with her beyond the fact we had cocks and she had a love pocket or two! So when my second friend rocked up I really thought it was sling your hook time. But I persevered and I looked at her and said, "What ya think?" Her reply? "In for a penny, in for a pound." So three shots later and some vodka for the journey, we pile into the cab at 7.30 only an hour after meeting!

So we are on the way back and it all kicks off just as we are rolling down the embankment. We've got her tits out, she's got some coke, so we have a couple of sniffs in the back of the black cab. My mate then pulls her panties down by her ankles and starts having a fiddle. Anyways we arrive at her place in South London. Through the door and straight to the kitchen table. It's quite a cool looking place and luckily her flatmates are out, so we've the place to ourselves; beers and music and we are on our way.

She racks up some more coke and we are all gathered around and, semi-naked, she led the way. Christ, she had some balls. My mate is all over her. She's loving it having lines hoovered off her. The funniest sight! My mate is really going for it while the two of us are watching and we are kind of chatting and he's practically sawing her from the inside, friggin' her so fast he has sweat pouring from him. He's so caught up he doesn't notice us watching. After a while he then comes back around to face us and the line of the year comes out of his mouth: "It's like fucking Rumpelstiltskin!!!" Sadly the coke kicked in and we all went a little soft although to be fair I was just about holding it together so was putting in a little performance. After a while we all go for it; my mate's being sucked off, another is fingering her. Then we have this great idea: let's grab a shower, it was like a scene out of Caligula. This is where I coined a new phrase. It was her fantasy to be filled up in every hole, so we all jumped into her shower, my mate sat down, she's on his cock, I'm up her arse and other mate in her mouth. This, we coined, is 'tupperwaring' (making her air tight!). It went on until half ten but my mate headed downstairs and hailed a cab so we all said our goodbyes and went back to a party in town, leaving her by herself. Even though she wanted to come with us we made some bullshit and left her alone which was probably a little harsh.

About 1.30am that same night still with the horn, me and my mate who shouted Rumpelstiltskin jumped in a cab back to hers, woke her up now fully charging, loaded with booze, no drugs and just dragged her to the bedroom and properly fucked her. We were dripping; we both tag-teamed her again, this time coming all over her face in turns. She was a real wrong 'un. We had a quick shower and scampered home! It is amazing as I still see her occasionally when we run into each other at showbiz parties or in Soho. That's always interesting especially as I can't remember her name!

2 Helping out a friend

For most people Monday nights normally mean a chance to relax, a chance to catch up with soaps on TV, or perhaps to start that no-drinking-for-a-week promise. For me it invariably means going to a showbiz party. The place where the liggers like me can be seen drinking free champagne, listening to dull speeches, and drinking more champagne. However I always see these launches/PR events and the like as a way to bring my mates together and get smashed for free. The usual drill is to rock up at 7pm, do the paparazzi photos outside, air kiss a couple of crappy celebrities, and then tuck into the booze. Now the beauty of having your proper mates there means that it's like being in your local boozer, plus if you are lucky you can pick up some minor celebrity and take back a goody bag. So after a few drinks the party wasn't going anywhere but we were slightly lit up so we headed off to a favourite members' club I knew around the corner. We were half cut when we got there. We did a bit of karaoke, few more drinks, and now we've got the horn!

Now being a Monday, it's unlikely you will find many clubs that are busy but my friend knew a club around the corner which is in Soho where you can get drinks and score coke off the waiters so not all would be lost if there were no women. I've had more nights in this place than I care to remember, had a blow job in the toilet, fucked in the stairwell and no one ever really complains. There is probably some CCTV footage floating about with me going hell for leather smashed at 1am. Anyways, it's half eleven when we bowl up, the doormen recognise me and we head straight into the VIP area. Personally I think it's a little sad just spending time in a VIP room but, that said, we were all straight bar one so thought it a little easier to chill and look for the odd fag hag from the calm velvet seats. Ten minutes in and my friend was getting a bit anxious. We'd been out a few hours, had a couple of lines and not a bird in sight. His exact words were: "Fuck this!" Off he goes; I'm assuming a stroll around the club to the toilets or maybe to leave. I kid you not, a minute later he rocks up with this bird I vaguely recognise (turns out she is a fashion photographer). Bit of a hello and we all know the score so me, my mate and gay friend get this girl's coat and we are off. Strange old taxi ride back as we don't even know her name. So me and my mate start kissing her bit tame at first but, like I said, we don't know her name and she doesn't know us from Adam!

Before we continue let me describe how she looks: blonde, pert little titties with that kind of loose black top (biker T-shirt-esque), no bra, tight black jeans, boots and a fairly pretty face, Scandinavian-looking, well she was Swedish... bit of an arse but nothing too shocking! Anyways we pile into my mate's Chelsea flat about midnight, through the door me and my gay mate rack up a couple of lines and while we are in the kitchen my friend who stole her from the club has got her tits out. He looks at me and says, "Have a suck!" to which my gay mate takes that as his cue to hit the sack. Probably the funniest thing watching my mate manhandle this girl's breast whilst I manoeuvre my tongue to lick them.

After some heavy breast petting he strips her naked and luckily she is well maintained downstairs. Nothing worse than Micronesia staring at you! She really starts to get into this.

She takes his cock out and I strip naked and after some failed attempts to get him hard (the coke was fairly strong) she starts going at mine. I've always had this way of focusing in a Zen-like way to get hard and to stop myself coming. Fortunately it was Zen o clock! She started sucking my cock whilst my mate was fingering her from behind. Once she was wet enough she sat on my cock, heat of the moment bareback, she started really riding me. I've got a fairly big penis but to take it all in and grind down hard was impressive, so much so I had that pelvic bruising for two days! After ten minutes or so I realised my mate had moved to the sofa and was just watching. It was hilarious; he couldn't get hard so was rubbing his cock like a fourteen-year-old desperately trying to join in.

Being a good mate, I moved her to the lovely doggy position for maximum carpet burnage (we are in the lounge). This way he could look at her while I fucked her hard from behind! After a few minutes, eureka, he started to rise to the occasion at which point she moved back to riding me, a favourite of hers. For me it's cool as long as the bird is energetic and rubs herself off at the same time. So she's going at it and I'm looking over his shoulder as he walks around the coffee table cock in hand, wetting it with saliva. He crouches down and she knows he is there! So he's crouched down behind her and he starts fingering her arsehole and, sure enough, in his cock goes. Bless her, she gave a little yelp but we were off riding literally the arse off her. She didn't grumble too much and we must have both gone through seven or eight positions. One of the funniest moments was when we high-fived. I know it sounds terrible but being able to high-five over the head of a bird you are spit roasting is priceless. Needless to say, we fucked her for hours. To this day I can't remember her name and if I bumped into her in the street I probably wouldn't recognise her. Ruthless, but another very funny moment and not bad for a Monday!

3 Twelve hours of pure filth

This is one of the filthiest twelve hours I've had in a long time. It was an unassuming Tuesday until about 1pm when I get a phone call off a friend of mine who is an actor asking if I wanted a four-way with two glamour girls. Let me explain: this is a friend who has a serious bird. He works on TV and directs porn; he is properly wrong. Now I was doing some interviews all day so could only get away at 4pm but my obvious answer was, "Where and when?!" He said his place which was a good half-hour from where I was working in a hotel in central London.

Not to worry; the minute I'd finished I hailed a cab, quick taxi ride and I was off to his flat. I arrive through the door stone-cold sober and am greeted by a statuesque beauty with the most humungous bolt-ons! She was dressed in lingerie and a light green slip over the top. She was a bit jittery; apparently she'd just done some coke; it was 4pm! God love London. My other mate walked through and there is that weird atmosphere where they had both just fucked and were chilling and I was there fully clothed, make-up on from just being interviewed and clearly in a different head space. Plus her mate wasn't there so it was going to just be myself, my actor mate and huge tits. Not all bad but for the amount of effort I put in, I thought there would be two birds going at it lesbos style.

Now, like most glamour girls, chat isn't their forte. That said, she looked alright and was really well groomed. So I thought, fuck it, it'll be a laugh to tuck into her with my mate. The thing is, her usual stomping ground is some of the West End clubs where footballers are her prey. For me these types of women are bloody horrific: leeches! So I down my drink and said, "Come on then, let's head upstairs." My mate's clearly been fucking her in there as there is that smell of pussy and sweat. Now bear in mind she is fit, but she has bolt-ons and an aggressive sexual manner like hers doesn't really do it for me plus I was convinced that was cum on her thigh. So I drop my clothes on the floor while she does a line and they look at me cock hanging in the wind. Properly like a scene out of a porno. If only I could tell you who I'd been interviewing just forty minutes earlier to this scene: phenomenal! So I join them on the bed and think I'll have a little lick of her bold pussy, lovely and clean and nice and juicy. Ten minutes in I can see my strokes are really wasted energy (she's numb from the drugs) so I ask for a blowy. She obliges and it is probably one of the worst ever. For someone who does this for a living she was clearly going through the motions, although she did have a knack of spitting on my cock. Hilarious to watch as she thought it was sexy! My mate meanwhile was fucking her behind, his eyes bulging from the pill he'd obviously taken. We did take it in turns and not for love nor money there is no way I'm coming, so after an hour I suggest a boozer! We all agree, have a line and a couple of shandies. I make my excuses and head off back to central London stinking of threesome!

Now normally you head back for a wash, purge yourself, have a cold drink and move on. I however had a date with a bird in town to go to a premiere. I was slightly apprehensive as she was quite well known; in fact she'd made a few tabloids but she seemed like a sweet girl and she'd been blown out by some minor pop star so I thought I'd go along. We had a drink, went in to watch the film having walked down the red carpet. I really didn't want to be photographed with her so made my excuses and got pictured alone. She didn't know why. Of course I just said, "This is about you, you do it alone!"

Anyways the film wasn't up to much so we

dipped out and went for a couple around the corner. Surprisingly she had alright banter. So we got a little closer and after a few more drinks went to the film-after party. The usual minor celebs waiting to see the real stars and free champagne and canapés. Now she'd got some coke so I was never going to eat but I knew some of the actors so did the rounds. Cut to half an hour later and she was all over me. So we headed outside as I really didn't want to be seen with her. As soon as we are out of the club she's clawing at me wildly and there and then she started sucking me off in a dark alley off Soho. Feeling a little paranoid we stopped and lucky we did because three showbiz journos walked around the corner! We went to a club she always goes to, and sure enough loads of footballers were there. I'm convinced she'd screwed the lot, ha.

It's now about 1am, we make our excuses and leave. On the way back she's got my cock out in the cab, I'm playing with her fake tits, just like the ones from earlier! We get through her door and get straight to it, fucking everywhere. She starts snorting coke off my cock, I'm licking her arsehole and then I get a brainwave, bum love!

She is made for fucking, stunning gym-toned physique, Playboy bunny type but with dark hair! The only lube I can find is virgin olive oil. That'll do and she doesn't care so imagine the scene: me and fuck buddy going at it covered in oil and specks of shit. It was daylight when we finished. I was shagged out. One of the most depraved twelve hours. I was so sore I couldn't move for a day but what a fuck. I actually met up with her once more and fucked her mate while she watched, all very twisted but a great story for the lads

4 Just like Roman times

The strange thing about prostitutes is half the time they are doing it under duress, trafficked and against their will. Sometimes they are willing and genuinely do it for money like the escorts you see on the online ads. As a rule I don't really like brasses as I feel it's like shooting fish in a barrel. Considering how easy it is to meet women in London it seems a little sad. That said, a friend of mine was in town. It was only meant to be a bit of a pub crawl, food, a club and maybe chip off back home. Except he'd brought a couple of mates who live in the Middle East where prostitution is accepted and yet frowned upon; amazing the mixed messages over there! Now they were loaded, the kind of money where four bottles of Cristal at £600 a pop is not a problem! So we started at their hotel just off Park Lane, four other mates joined, so nine of us ready to get smashed. They'd booked a suite with a gym, sauna, Jacuzzi, four bedrooms. I mean this is the kind of place rock stars and kings stay in whilst in town! Probably at a cost of 10k a night!

We all had a few drinks there. They'd loaded up trays of beers on ice and bottles and bottles of champagne and so much vodka I could feel my kidneys wincing! Just three drinks in, they concocted a plan, much to my dismay. The plan? We'd go out for a few, then head to this whore house we know, more like a nightclub with a bar and small dance floor. It is so wrong and right under the noses of everyone in central London! We bowl up about 10pm all lit up. Through the door, and what do we see but at least thirty brasses all sat around, guys chatting and so on. Bearing in mind there were nine guys, the girls were either thinking ker-ching, or shit, I was about to knock off work. Well, a friend of mine with balls like marrows just went up to four birds and said, "You are coming with me!" The rest of us grabbed a couple but I wasn't feeling that good about it as for me it's just a posh wank! Anyhow we took ten back with us, easy as that. We paid upfront and we were to tip them as we fucked them if you like! If you've ever been with a brass it's the strangest exchange of goods; it's clinical, loveless, but you get a good feeling at the end!

So imagine the scene: nineteen people, half prostitutes, tits everywhere, strolling through one of the oldest hotels in London. In any other hotel we'd be kicked out but my mate had bribed the front desk plus we had one of their suites. So we've all got back to the hotel room and we all start making small talk with these girls. It looked like a school disco: some of us in corners, some gathered around sharing stories. Now what is the etiquette when you have ten brasses in a hotel room? From the offset we agreed we would not lock any doors and it was a free-for-all whatever happened. So it's half an hour in and we are getting closer to the birds when the door swings open and in walks my mate Steve stark bollock naked, cock at half mast with a used condom hanging off the end filled with his conker water! He then whipped it off his knob, wrapped it around the chandelier, and, chuckling, grabbed another bird and went into the bedroom!

That was our cue: the party changed there and then. We all dropped the small talk and I pile off with this Chinese girl, small tits, curvy arse with a fringe, the ultimate Asian fantasy! So after a little haggle about £30, I took her into the Jacuzzi room and she got down on her knees and started sucking my cock, all the while the bubbles of the Jacuzzi fizzing on to the floor. So I didn't hear when my mates came in, but I thought fuck it, be funny for them to watch. One even tried to join in although she would only do me as she had rules!! After I shot my glue with this average pump, I walked through to the lounge area and it was like something out of Caligula: bodies everywhere and every now and then someone would get up and go grab a drink and get stuck in.

Now I was watching this and feeling horny so I picked up a blonde Russian. Now Russians can be immense in bed or lazy (depending on how fit they are!). This one was blonde, big tits, tiny waist. Bugger is my mate had only just finished shagging her. But sod it, I gave her £40 and tucked in. It was grim to be fair, smelling all your mates all over these birds. But funny as fuck. It was about 3.40am and we are all sat around on a slight unwind but I really wanted to screw a bird with my mate so we found the most likely to partake. A pretty ropey bird but OK body, dark hair and completely smooth downstairs. Sadly I hardly had any change on me and nor did my mate Al. So we haggled, and in the end we agreed to have a three-way, funniest sight! For £15 I banged her from behind while my mate skull fucked her, and another pal sat at the end of the bed wanking. After I'd shot my glue I went through for a drink, skint of sperm and skint of cash. I started chatting with this girl called Olga, who was nineteen, new in town.

Olga seemed sweet although half an hour earlier she had been noshing my mate in the kitchen area. We chatted and I said I'd love to fuck and she was keen. It then came to the subject of cash; having none on me we hit a crossroads. So being ever the improviser I suggested I treat her to some cunnilingus in return for some sex for free. Amazingly she agreed when I showed her the length of my tongue. One proviso, she had to shower; I mean she had cum on her leg!

This is when I did something that most people think is a little on the grim side. I licked her out not once but probably eight times. Each time she kept exploding. I've never had a bird like that. It was like stroking a stray cat, you know they just really appreciate it! Then I fucked her and went to sleep. I woke up to find a note from Olga giving her personal number and asking to meet up some time. I never did call but what a night it was. An absolute state that room but I finally know how rock stars live!

5 The happiest ending

I've told this story to a female friend who always masturbates to it, whenever she wants to fantasise, so maybe this can tick some lady boxes! Where I live there is a spa and massage suite, the kind of place you can get acupuncture, a hair cut, and massages. They always have lots of beauticians walking around and they all love to be flirted with. Let me stress it is all legit and, being in Knightsbridge, fairly exclusive; certainly the last place to imagine having sex!

Having been going there for months I was familiar with all the staff, and this one girl always used to give me the eye. We never spoke but she would always hold my stare. The problem was she was dating the owner, in fact one of the stylists told me she lived with him, but she had something! She had this sexy little uniform which was in black with a slit in the thigh. She had a stunning face and beautiful eyes, bit of an arse, but she had huge tits; just thinking of them puts a smile on my face.

Now one day we got chatting, albeit briefly as everyone was around including her boss/boyfriend. But I had to find a way to give her my number. It was such a sneaky manoeuvre. I made sure I asked her for some info on beauty products whilst still making small talk as I didn't even know her name. When she handed it over I slipped her my number. She never flinched. Right there and then I knew what the possibility was. I got my products and walked out cool as a cucumber. It could've gone either way: imagine if I had misread the signals, she could've freaked!

Couple of days now passed and I remember it was a Thursday morning about 7.30. Strange time to get a text but as it happened I was still up kind of tossing and turning as I had been out the night before. With the morning horn this couldn't have come at a better time. She sent me a text saying, 'Hey, gorgeous, how are you?' Two texts later and I've got a video clip of her frigging herself and playing with her massive milky tits! So horny at this point I said, 'Why don't I come in for a massage and you can show me the real thing.' Now I don't know this bird at all and know it will be risky as she lives with her boyfriend and he will be there at the salon! Is it going to be a stitch up as I rock up? Sod it, I thought, so horny as you like I made an appointment and 10am I'm at the salon.

One of the assistants shows me up to the beauty room and she is there all coy and is being really polite and normal as if I'm a punter having a massage, so I lie down and we start talking. I'm now thinking this is going nowhere fast as I can't seem to steer the conversation. She then tells me she was out all night and did loads of drugs and was still really horny. Ears are now pricked up and I'm in. The problem is it's only a forty-five minute massage and then I have to head downstairs and pay. So as she massages my chest and front of shoulder, I unbutton her top and her tits flap out and into my face! She loves me licking her nipples and, without prompting, she pulls out my cock and starts to wank me off covering my cock in oil. After five minutes or so I shoot all over myself, clean up and bugger off. She fucking loved the naughtiness of it with her boyfriend working downstairs and I loved the fact I'd got wanked off by my masseuse. Needless to say all afternoon in between clients she would send me photos of herself. Now we hadn't had sex yet and I'd love to fuck her as her pussy looked amazing in the phone pictures, but it was going to be really difficult due to our living situations.

About a week later I got my chance. About 8pm comes a text message. Bearing in mind I've friends at mine and getting away from them would be murder, I pretended I had to pop to the shops for some wine. The text I got would make you do the same! It read, 'I'm at supper with my boyfriend next to the shop, meet me outside and let's fuck' or along those lines. Basically she'd left the restaurant to let us in to her salon to fuck while he was next door! Risky, I know, but this girl was amazing, twenty-two and pure filth.

So we met up outside the shop. It was still light so I was certain I was going to get busted. She undoes the door, unsets the alarm, and the minute we walked in we started tongueing, me grabbing her tits, but she wants some coke first so she chopped up a line for us both, which instantly makes the whole experience even more debauched. No mucking about, we are straight into fucking on the reception floor. I just remember those magnificent massive breasts pert and full, wow just thinking about them will last a lifetime. We didn't have long but I still licked her out and finger banged her. She couldn't get enough and it soon became obvious she was a squirter, literally jetting out, amazing! It was everywhere, all over my face, my legs, her thighs, we fucked in all this lady juice for ten minutes, both came, quick clean up, she went back to the restaurant and I went home. I couldn't believe what had happened. I've never met anyone quite like her. Within thirty minutes of getting the text we'd met up, had some hoot and fucked silly without anyone ever knowing. My mates didn't even twig on and I rocked back cool as a cucumber and she was now sat with her boyfriend eating her main course. We would meet up again over the next two months or so for a while even indulging in three ways with her mates, but she was nuts and a little clingy. But what a great experience!

6 A few very wrong days

Picking up women at one point became so easy. I don't mean to come across as an arrogant sod, but it did. I suppose I developed a sure-fire technique. You can buy all the books you want, take part in those seminars in the States, but the real key is trial and error and, frankly, the confidence to not give a fuck if you get blown out. I was going through women so fast at one point my mates thought I had a sex addiction. I know it sounds far-fetched but it becomes like collecting trophies.

It was a really hot week in London a couple of years ago, the time when the papers are full of *we are hotter than Miami, hotter than Nigeria* etc. If you have spent time in London during the summer I challenge anyone to have a better time. The women all suddenly show too much flesh, everyone stays out drinking with all the pubs spilling out and generally the place becomes a better place to live! It was one of those weeks. A bunch of us had been going out Monday through to the Thursday as a mate was in town! His cousin was always about as she was studying at the local uni and loved a couple of drinks with some of us up the West End each night; she was really tidy, lovely cans, beautiful skin, half Chinese with the most amazing gym instructor-type body! So I'd been grafting her for a few nights, she had only just come out of a serious relationship and was surprisingly difficult to crack, but all the boys fancied her, so I had to win! The first night that we'd all gone out, done loads of sambucas, loads of wine, and at the end I took her back but only had a little kiss and cuddle. She then passed out drunk, as did I.

Happy as Larry as she is a cracker and when you

get fanny nabbed by a bird you get fanny nabbed! By that I mean she denied me which made me even more keen. Well, I do. So it's about 3 when there is a knock at the door. Quietly my mate whose cousin it is that I'm in bed with says, "Head to the spare room, some action!" Chucks two jonnies and heads off to bed. The funniest sight, my mate is trying to handle two birds that they've brought back so I give him a hand and we high-five over these birds. Now normally I would elaborate but all I can say is my mate was happy as he had a foursome and ticked a box but I was gutted as I liked the cousin who'd passed out. By doing this I could have blown my chance with her but the temptation was too high!

The next day comes by and we all start reminiscing about the night before. Guess what, the girl I like knows all about it and, worse, knows I'm seeing a bird as well! Now this was only the Monday and I figured a couple of nights of graft and she'd be all over me again. She was having none of it and on the Friday I was heading away for work, so thought Thursday is now or never!

I dressed up in my best clothes, I was tanned to the max, money in pocket and that kind of form you get which is a mixture of being hungover tired but happy as life is going your way. So we all meet up for a few drinks, bit of food and as usual guys are all over her and I know she is keen as she keeps looking over. She even tells me she thinks she loves me but I'm just too naughty for her. Undeterred I graft and graft, but alas nothing. She is so smashed after all the shots they stick her in a cab and I get hold of some hoot and rack up the biggest lines and hang out with all the ropey birds in this shitty club just off Mayfair. Anyways I meet these two backpacker types, alright looking, but nothing special and on the lash, gold-diggers looking for people with cash. Now I'm with some celebs so they figure we are good to lig off. These birds were nothing special but the thought of being blown out by the cousin fuelled me with guttedness, so the logical step was to get twisted and bang two random birds.

So at the end of the night five of us pile into a cab and head back to my mate's where the cousin is also staying and he has a small pool in the downstairs. Knowing the two backpackers are fair game I get them a drink, give them a line and chuck them in the pool naked. My mates are entertaining them, which gives me a chance to speak with the cousin who is upstairs asleep.

She is smashed but wakes up when I knock on the double doors. She opens them and jumps straight back into bed. I said, “It’s our last night, what do you reckon you and me sleep together.” But once again she tells me how bad I am, etc. I’m pleading and saying at least I’m honest with her unlike my mates who were doing just the same but getting away without her knowing so in her eyes they were little cherubs! So with as much arrogance as I can muster I said, “This is your last chance - either fuck me or I m going down to bang the backpackers.” She said, “No!” Honestly, I thought I was in, so what to do? I headed down to the pool, got the backpackers side by side and I finger puppet them both at the same time in the pool, fucking each of them one at a time while they watched my mate wank on the lounger.

She did tell me once more weeks later she was keen on me and really wanted to take it to the next level, but to be honest I really think it was the chase that gave me the horn and that is the problem. She never let me in and life is too short. Little does she know in that week I shagged six birds. Alright, so I may not have the most integrity but I've got some great stories.

7 What a dirty dirty dirty girl

This is probably tamer than most of my stories but the fact that she was married to a footballer, sober for a year and had never cheated on her partner, with me breaking down her back door for the first time, felt like a badge of honour. On top of that, she was very, very, very hot!!

I was out at a showbiz party in Soho that evening for the launch of a gallery; nothing special but it did allow me the opportunity to network! Anyway, my best mate, my editor and myself were getting tanked up and had taken delivery from a dealer so were on fire. We found ourselves in the latest faceless club in London where luckily enough I knew the promoter so we had a bottle of free booze and were surrounded by wannabee wags! Well, if you've ever spent time with a glamour model invariably they are nothing to look at up close and, as a rule, have shit chat! Well, this evening was nothing new. We were having a good time though as the booze was flowing and we were doing line after line, helped by the odd tongueing of the girl to our right!

About 1am, you notice other people on the prowl like yourself. I was looking across the dance floor and there was this blonde giving me the eye, repeatedly looking over. She was wearing a tight black dress, high heels, had blonde hair, light make-up and a cleavage to die for! She had the body of a swimwear model and a fairly pretty face, but I'm a perfectionist in that area! But those tits, they were big, milky and naturally pert. She kept looking which is really strange for a girl to be that full on. Normally the hotter they are the more aloof, but she was hot and clearly very keen.

She actually came over and planted herself next to me with her ugly mate; always seems to be the way, so I made her friend feel comfortable and played down the fact I fancied her mate more. After half an hour of small talk, I knew she was a part-time model and she was out on her weekly Thursday night clubbing, very dull!! I was chatting more and more when that moment comes up where we are locked in conversation and chatting eye to eye, so I went in for the kiss and she responded and hard.

Thinking my luck was in I was almost ready to get her coat and she drops the bombshell she was heading back to her boyfriend's. I thought she would have one. I delved a little deeper but she wouldn't say much about what he did, who he was, to be fair I didn't really care!! Two days had passed and I can only vaguely remember her but those tits had stuck in my mind! She finally drops me a text. What is wrong with this girl, she lives with her boyfriend, but you know when a bird is like that you can do whatever you want. She says she wants to meet up. So we arrange to meet near hers when he is away on a Saturday afternoon working.

I rock up not knowing what to expect. We had to be discreet which I thought strange and had to meet three streets down so no one would see me! We head to the local boozer. She has got shit chat. For me that's such a turn-off. You can be attractive and all that but bottom line for me is I'm only ever going to fuck you if you can't hold your own, not date you. I know that sounds just a little egotistical but being good-looking means fuck all if you can't back it up! You know the type, she doesn't ask questions and you think am I talking to much as she never helps the conversation flow! Anyhow a bottle of wine in and I've got my hand on her lap. I've swivelled around facing her now and we have a little play. As she is a little tipsy she suggests we head back to her place. In the car I'm showing off making her laugh and generally keeping the conversation energetic so she won't change her mind!

It was hilarious. We rock up to his house and he's got football stuff everywhere. The penny drops that he is a footballer, and I'm sat in his lounge with his missus a little too close for comfort but fuck it. I know she wants a fuck and, as it's our second date, why not! So we retire to the bedroom and start to play about. I lick her out but she can never come when she's been drinking, she says. That's a touch, straight to the sex then! Fifteen minutes in and I am loving it, seeing those magnificent perfect breasts bouncing up and down in front of me, whilst she is riding me. I reach around and start tickling her balloon knot, sure enough she is receptive. I ask has she ever had sex up the arse, her answer no, but she thinks she'd like it. So baby lotion later, I've got her on all fours whilst she's playing with her pussy. I'm fingering her arsehole and she is pushing back more and more and loving it, so two fingers, almost three, now time for my cock. I'm fucking her up the arse so hard her head is on the floor, arse on the bed, she is screaming, asking me to slap her, strangle her, it is almost like I've awoken some beast. It was slightly off-putting as his football pictures are all over the wall and I'm practically choking her. Turns out she loves it up the arse so much so that whenever we'd meet she'd want nothing up the pussy. She had a penchant for drugs, cheap hotels and she was a kinky bitch, used to pee on me and everything! She even got engaged to this guy when we were screwing. It was a fun time, and I'll never forget her as every time Match of the Day is on I see him. That said, they've just been relegated, so maybe not!

The Model

A little about Mr M: as the title suggests he is a model and a very good friend. Through the years I've worked with him and more importantly had many a great night out with him. He is one of those unassuming kind of guys; yes, he is a good-looking bloke and funny to boot but he isn't in your face. One of the reasons I think he has such a way with the ladies is that he is persistent. He also has this effeminate side to him. But this doesn't mean that he isn't one of the boys and doesn't like a drink. Trust me, he is an animal in that sense. It's just that he draws women to him because they trust him, they want to talk with him, and to this extent his technique is genius: befriend the ladies and then they are putty in his hands.

You will have seen Mr M in TV commercials, in many a high-street catalogue, and in Asia he is a bit of a celebrity. Through the years he has dated models, TV stars, it girls, strippers and a couple of supermodels. As a model he has travelled and lived in more than forty countries, earnt hundreds of thousands of pounds and has more stories than any other male model I've ever met. I'll let him tell his story now. Over to you, Mr M.

Making judgements about yourself at a young age is both difficult and dangerous but I was always sure about my love of the female form. As I became older and had the ability to see and then understand female sexuality I knew that girls and women are the greatest thing on this earth.

I just love the female body – it has so many different attributes. Yes, there are the obvious parts: ass, tits, legs, which strike a chord with your testosterone. But then there are the subtle parts as well: the little bits of skin that join arms to torso, the smooth curvature of a back or the perfect ankle. Personality is hugely important too. The dip of the eyes or flash of a smile fuel sexual anticipation and give an insight to the soul. It's no use looking like Gisele if you can't carry yourself and you just behave like a wallflower. More often than not these girls will not perform between the sheets.

Some guys have sex because they like to keep scores or brag to their mates or to boost their self-confidence. This is not me. I just love the female race though it is as much a blessing as a curse.

There is a moment on meeting every girl when you know if there is a chance that, at some point, you might have sex with her. It may be a slightly cheeky smile or a look that is held for a nanosecond longer than necessary. Yes, I love the sex, the animalistic uncontrolled passion with no taboos but this sometimes doesn't happen unless there is decent pent-up sexual frustration. When it does happen it's golden; no questions asked, just two bodies completely surrendering themselves to each other with complete disregard for any moral standards that society puts on us.

What do girls like about me? Tough call. All I can say is that, regardless of whether they like me or not, I always respect them. Yes, I'm vain and I want them all to like me but I realise that's impossible and impractical so I try to find a small connection and live the moment with each girl and each situation. That sounds wacky but I can do no better and I'm really against all that formulaic stuff that The Game offers. I think it really misses the delicate nuances of each situation…

1 The one with the boyfriend

Christina and I met on a modelling job. She was a typically unassuming girl who talked earnestly about her boyfriend for the first two hours we were there. But, as Shakespeare said, 'Methinks she doth protest too much.' We went out for a drink after work but, having seen her in her underwear during the shoot all day, I knew she was certainly quite a wild and attractive girl. Of course, after a couple of drinks, things heated up and I got that sense without being arrogant that, potentially, she might fancy me as well. We went on and did the club thing and went back to mine, had a couple of drinks – things were looking good. Nothing happened that night which was fine. I certainly did not push it. I knew she was a sensitive girl. And sometimes with these kinds of girls you don't want to push it. I was happy to save myself for the next round and without being overconfident I knew she was into me. The second time we met up two days later there were no subtleties or flirtations. After half an hour in the pub we went back to my flat in Camden about 7pm. Christina was unbelievable; she was sensitive yet slutty, she was a mix between a librarian and a whore, and all rolled into this one complex but very sensitive individual. The sex started very slowly. She undressed me but she would not let me undress her at all. This upset me as I thought she was the biggest tease in the world. She knew exactly what she was going to do. She stripped off very slowly, lay back on the bed and peeled off her jeans to reveal matching panties. We went from a bit of passionate kissing to her going down on me—she had that ability to lick, suck and touch in all the right places whilst keeping her eye contact. We had sex in about four or five positions and this is where it got interesting because I knew she was up for anything, or at least got that impression. So at that point I started nudging my cock just at the base of her pussy, at the same time rubbing my finger around the rim of her arsehole. She did not knock my hand out of the way which is always a promising sign. And I just remember her turning around at one point and saying in her Chicago accent, "Are you trying to fuck me up the ass?" to which I just smiled as I was unsure as to whether that meant do you want to or are you going to? From there on in, I played around a little more, gave her a little rimming and bizarrely, within about another minute, she let out a little howl, a kind of frustrated but sexy howl, and I stuck my dick in her arse. After that we had the wildest sex for the next three hours. I put off coming at least twice. Eventually I did come and stopped for about another hour. Then I started again and it was the same routine all over again. I suppose the comedy part, and like most things in sex there is a comedy part, is that, about half an hour after I'd come all over her back and face and had my cock in her arse and mouth, the phone rang and she answered and of course it was the boyfriend, the wonderful boyfriend. I'll never forget just looking at her with a little bit of cum dribbling down her face and her saying to her boyfriend, "It's not a good time, I'll call you back in a bit."

2 The young one

Osaka is one of the most boring cities I've ever travelled to. Although I model in London as part of my work I have to travel all around the world. Now I'd been there for six weeks and the best thing that had happened was a hand job from a stripper. But that was all about to change in a very positive fashion after this dry patch. A friend of mine came down, she was about twenty-eight; she had a reputation for enjoying the company of men on a loose basis which was good and our times started off in a very platonic, in my opinion, non-sexy friend-like way. However there was always an ingredient in there that could've developed. We'd flirted before but so far nothing had come to life. Around the same time another model I knew had flown into town for work from Tokyo. She was only seventeen. I'd spoken with her briefly a few times when I was in Tokyo. So we were invited to one of these house parties one night, the kind where there are nibbles everywhere and loads of drinks knocking about. These can be fun and lead to some naughtiness occasionally, certainly when you are in an isolated environment, and lead to some potential flings, certainly when you are in a Japanese city. We all drank, got a little bit more drunk and eventually had to head off to pick up more alcohol. In these situations you can manipulate things so that you are one on one with the girl you may want to get hold of. So the young girl, Sophie, and Michelle, the older model, went out together leaving the other friends there so I had these two to myself. Michelle started to come across a little keen but maintained that Sophie preferred me and she was happy to step out of the picture. Anyway we went to this karaoke bar, and Sophie and I found ourselves a little private dark corner. Now Sophie was only seventeen but to be honest I don't have a problem with that. The law states the girl has to be sixteen in order for it to be legal to have sex with her, and I'm a law-abiding citizen! Some guys have a more moral and, may I say, pious disposition towards this and see it as being wrong. I don't—law says sixteen, she's seventeen – let's proceed. She certainly didn't move like a seventeen-year-old; she clearly had a lot of experience. This girl was no virgin! Being Canadian as well, Canadians in my experience also tend to be more liberal so it was all going well: the way she moved her hips and her tight hourglass curvy arse. Things were looking promising, so back to the karaoke room, things were progressing. There was a lot of touching and muttering and feeling. She was a little over the top but you take that as it can always lead to something special. However at that point this Japanese security guard stopped us as I was about to put my tongue in the crack of her arse. So we went back to my friend's and soon went off to the nightclub. Of course by this point we were getting a little more drunk. I was chatting with Michelle who was back on the scene. Being even more drunk and buoyed by my almost sexual experience with Sophie, I began to quiz her about her reputation in a subtle fashion. I'd heard great stories of Michelle. Apparently she states in a very unsubtle way how she likes giving blow jobs and how amazing she is at this. I picked up on this indirectly and had heard how good she was in bed. She was enjoying the attention and her confidence was increasing. Meanwhile Sophie was up and dancing as seventeen-year-olds tend to do in nightclubs—so she was out of the way. Now there was no jealousy here as Michelle had a boyfriend as did many of these girls, but there was definitely intrigue on both our parts. It was going well when she leaned in and, seeing Sophie on the dance floor, said, "Come with me to the toilet, I've got such a fetish I want to show you." So I was thinking this could go either way: it could be something rather crude or something amazing. Chances were it was going to be fucking phenomenal. So she pulled me straight into the ladies' toilets and, barging past these dumbstruck Japanese girls, straight into a cubicle. She then instantly pulled down my pants and started sucking my cock. Yes, she wasn't lying, she was good. She was really good. However I'm not the best in these situations as I always get paranoid that somebody is going to look in or pull me out of the nightclub. Plus the fact I really had my eye on securing Sophie. As well as the fact that I was in the girl's toilet and there was every chance Sophie could come in and ruin my chances and that would be game over with the seventeen-year-old. Anyway, we didn't really stop and she sucked away for a few minutes and I thought this was sexy but I could definitely turn up the volume because it was all going one way. She was showing me her skills, her fetish, but I was giving her nothing. I waited a little bit longer until I realised I wasn't going to come and I just picked her up off the floor where she was kneeling. I bent her over the toilet, gave her a tiny bit of spit and stuck it straight in. She was screaming at this point, kind of not overly loud but the kind of scream she was trying to keep under her breath and trying to keep under control, although she was far from in control. I remember flushing the toilet two or three times trying to disguise the noise, although I've no idea if it worked or not. I kept on for a few more minutes, turned her around and came all over her tits. Standard performance! She enjoyed that, I enjoyed it. I gave her a hug and a kiss telling her she was particularly good. I said, "Let's go back in, I'll buy you a cocktail." So back inside the club we've got our drinks and within a few moments Sophie came over and said, "Hey, guys, what's been going on?" Completely clueless! Moving on from that we all ended up in a drunken mess that night back at my place. I still wanted to show Sophie that I was an upstanding gentleman and citizen, respectful and all that bullshit which I did. Wind on a couple of nights and I knew I'd got Sophie's respect and probably slightly in my head I'd been putting it off as I was starting to notice her age because she was only seventeen. But we arranged to meet at hers. She arrived at the door with a tight red vest on and these fantastic arse- and leg-hugging sports pants. It revealed every sexy bit of her and I'll never forget her walking down those stairs. Her shape was fantastic even though she had small tits but with an amazing arse and tight waist. Anyway she took me upstairs to hers and cooked me dinner and I pretended I was more tired than I was so I could lie down in her bed and watch her make me some food. Of course it progressed from there as I lay looking at the surroundings of this really small Japanese flat that utilized every inch of the apartment. Amazingly she pinned me down and said, “Right, you do exactly what I say or we’ll start all over again.” I couldn’t believe it! Out of nowhere I’ve got this seventeen-year-old dominatrix telling me what to do. It doesn’t get any better than this! She then proceeded to take my clothes off and then hers down to her underwear, massaging and caressing every part of my body, turning me over and playing with my legs. I thought I was going to come right there. Just softly kissing up my thighs, around my balls and my cock. Jeez, I was about to explode but I didn’t want to do that and have her start all over again, me being this real drip, not the best start. However she carried on and I focused. There were a few close moments but she gave me the best blow job I’d ever had. Now that’s not because she was young and didn’t expect it but simply because she was the best. She knew every trick in the book: tongues, deep throat, everything, all concocted together in perfect synergy to make my best blow job; in fact anyone’s best blow job! It was almost like she had studied this, she could write books about this. I’ve no idea how long this took – maybe ten minutes to half an hour and to finish it off… well, I could leave this to your imagination, but it would be cruel not to tell you. She knew the first spurts were coming and she swallowed the first little bits and when it came to the second push she took her lips right to the tip, all over her chin, her chest and rubbed it all over her body using every part. What a pair of girls!

3 The beautiful one

The first time travelling always gets you excited, when you are in a new place, with all these new experiences ahead of you and girls to meet and nights out to be had. That was certainly the case when I flew into Tokyo. It was my first time there and I had just flown in from London. I was taking the whole place in which was amazing, but what was even better was the taking in of just how many seemingly beautiful girls there were around. Now, of course, you take one hundred beautiful sexy girls as a ballpark figure and you can halve that as the ones who have boyfriends and won't be cheating on them. And you can half that again to the ones who are a little fucked up. Then you can half that again for the ones who aren't interested in you. So you are probably down to about 12% of your target zone of the original one hundred sexy, attractive model girls there were in that crazy city.

One of these was lucky enough to be in my agency – a truly stunning girl, Polish, properly out of my league girl. But, you know, you make a few snippets of conversation, you catch a look as I did in the first couple of weeks, and you hope that at some point you have the opportunity to press home this advantage. The opportunity came one night at an agency party. Bianca was there; she had come with her then boyfriend. But you could tell there was no real interest and we were having a laugh and a joke. At the end of the night they had a fallout and she headed to the nightclub by herself. It was at that point I knew there might be more than just beauty to her. She was charming but when she danced, even though she was a shy girl, there was some sexuality running through her that surpassed the shy persona she liked to give off.

That night was quite simple: we had a little dance and I left her knowing that I liked her but nothing happened. Wind this on to the following week and we finally got together. Fancying this girl so much, the couple of sex sessions were quite timid affairs as we got to know each other, but there were always those one or two minutes when during the sex session I would try something different, sliding my hand across her arse or indeed, when it came to the second time, coming all over her tits and just seeing her reaction, her reaction on both these occasions, so it was game on for the next stage. Now there is one thing having a dirty girl, and there is something about a dirty and attractive girl, but when you have a dirty and absolutely stunning girl, well, that is so much more enjoyable. She had turquoise eyes that you could just fall into, her cheekbones were fantasy book and her body was very model-like, not very curvy but everything in place. She looked good, she tasted good, everything was great.

With only a week to go before I had to head back to London, it came to me that there was nothing to lose, so it was time for me to turn up the volume sexually. We went out one night and surprisingly enough she suggested we take some Ecstasy and I was fine with that, although not having taken it an awful lot I was a little wary.

However, with Bianca, I wasn't going to reject this opportunity. So we took some and we were in this nightclub and she suddenly turned into this mischievous young girl. She started dancing all sexily, muttering under her breath something about role-play. Now role-play sounds sexy enough in English but said with a Polish accent it sounds nothing short of fantastic. She had mentioned a few times about having older boyfriends, which is pretty bog standard when it comes to Eastern European girls. Most of them in their twenties have relationships with guys in their late thirties or early forties which she had done. So she started telling me about how there was this guy who was a schoolteacher and she was in her last year at school and she had had an affair with him. I picked up on this and thought how this would be the perfect form of role-play, and all this was happening within about fifteen minutes of us dropping the Ecstasy tablet. She was dancing far too sexily in the nightclub so I thought it best to change the environment. So we went back to her place and I remembered her having this white shirt, black skirt combo outfit that she had worn one night, so I suggested she change into that, which she thought was an excellent idea. I remember waiting tentatively in her flat and out she came – the most stunning girl I'd ever seen, but with pigtails, white shirt, black tie, black short skirt and stockings which came just an inch below her skirt and showed off that little bit of intrigue which were her pinky thighs.

She then started going into this bizarre teenage girl mode. OK, I thought and I went with it just checking she wasn't going nuts and that it wasn't the Ecstasy coming on too strong. She started asking what lessons was Sir going to show her today and so of course, not one to retire from or indeed opt out of such role-play, I improvised and used the cupboard as the piano and got her to sit down beside me as I carried on with the lesson. Slowly, as the imaginary lesson progressed, I put my hand up her skirt and started to rub her pussy. I said, "You can't tell anyone about this or I'll get the sack. You mustn't tell your classmates." She liked this very much and kept firmly in her character. I even suggested extra tuition at my house and then, should anyone find out, she would be punished! After a while I pinned her against the wall, lifted up her skirt, pulled down her pants, turned her around and stuck my tongue straight up her arse and in her pussy. She let out a yelp, mimicking the teenager she obviously was when this had last happened to her. Then, keeping her in this position, I took her over to where there was a partition and in the middle a central beam. I put her arms around this partition beam and tied her up with her schoolgirl tie. She put up a little bit of a struggle but this just suggested she was loving every minute of it and was excited about what was going to happen next. Holding her in this position, I started stroking her long legs and spread them as I stood behind. She was now ready and I slowly put myself in gradually building up to a solid rhythm. By this point I'd pulled her tits out of her white cotton bra and had undone one of her pigtails. She looked so vulnerable and so sexy; I made her beg me to untie her which she did. However the quid pro quo for this was that she was going to have to let me do what I wanted to her as she hadn't finished her lesson—naughty girl. With this I finally let her go, took her over the bed, and untied and moved her into four or five different positions, back to front, putting my tongue inside her arse, but not my cock - she was just too small! I made her beg for every last drop of cum from my cock which she agreed to.

The finishing position was fantastic. I remember her with her beautiful long legs and her arched back bent over the bed with one pigtail and her beautiful eyes just turning back to me in a very feline fashion. Of course I had to live up to my promises as well so, with a last few thrusts, I came from her waist and loads came flying out landing on her chin, her chest, all over her face. She seemed to enjoy this, then froze for a second. Then, in porn star fashion, she licked up every last drop, but with her face still a naughty schoolgirl character.

4 The intelligent one

There is something about intelligent girls that has intrigued me for a long time. You obviously know they are intelligent but you don't know anything about their sexuality because usually intelligent girls are so clever and bright that they don't show you anything about their sexuality. Instead they keep it hidden, using it as a power tool and backing it up with their intelligence or saving it for a special occasion. The bottom line is you won't know if they are sexually astute or boring, you'll never know if they are a rock star in bed or boring; you'll have to leave it up to your imagination. If you take that as an example, I'll give you an anomaly: Easter European girls. Consider these women often described as gold-diggers in the sense that they want more than just the charm of a potential mate; they want champagne, expensive clubs and gifts. So the passion is surpassed by the fiscal gain and frankly makes the whole experience very unsexy. You really can't tell what they are like in bed. The reason I'm telling you about both these stereotypes is that once I met this Russian girl. From the off I could tell she was extremely intelligent. She was also beautiful and had a great body. She wasn't overtly intelligent, she was humble and, above all, a nice girl. It was hard to get a spark or even any flirtation going. It was almost like flirtation was below her because she was so intelligent. She didn't do it like it was a frivolous waste of time. Through the years we bumped into each other in different countries, and I helped her from time to time, in particular with some advance English papers that she was studying for and I had gained some respect and brownie points for that.

There was another occasion when she was a little bit bored and agitated. On previous occasions I'd asked her out for a drink and she had flatly refused saying she had to study and referring also to a boyfriend that she always had. So it was three years and one day from our first meeting that Julia actually asked me if I'd like to go for a coffee. I thought she must need help with another English lesson. I was okay with that, so we met up for a coffee and she said, "Come on, let's go for a drink," which surprised me as she had a boyfriend. I was now a little bemused as to what was going on. Normally she dressed down, wearing jeans and plain tops and a jacket. That night she was wearing a skirt and, as she was a model, I knew she had a great figure. But wow, what legs! She was wearing these little ankle boots as if they were straight from the streets of New York or London, not your average Eastern European girl. She had style and class to back up her intelligence. So things progressed in the usual way and we had a couple of drinks and after a while we made it back to my flat. Very cliché, I know, but I offered her a massage and even though it lacked spontaneity it was successful. Anyway she also gave me a little bit of a massage. Then, all of a sudden, she pinned me to the bed taking control and pulling up her skirt revealing these frilly French knickers. Then she started kissing me – nothing more said. But I wanted to take it more slowly as I felt she was pulling me in only to knock me back. So I was a little more reticent, not wanting to pounce and come on too heavy in a manner I normally would with any girl if they were coming on this strong. By now I was between her legs and she was beautifully clean-shaven. I wasn't quite sure if she had done it for me or specifically for this date, but she was exquisite and unlike one or two previous experiences with Russian girls she smelt fantastic between her legs. So we stripped down; she was in her underwear but with her boots still on, I was in my underwear. We slowly ventured towards the bed. There was a lot of huffing and puffing and gasps, the kind you can only get from three years of pent-up frustration. The whole three years I'd been thinking she was only after my help with her studies so you can imagine how I felt that, after all this time, we could've been doing more than just studying. But perhaps it wouldn't have happened without the long wait!

So I'd got her on the bed, legs spread as wide as you could imagine, pussy open, hips grinding, gasping. I knew now she was genuinely just up for a shag, so things progressed through a series of different positions and ranging from your standard positions to those more extreme filthy, energetic Kama Sutra like moves. She was surprisingly agile as well, using her legs and body like she was a highly experienced lady, wrapping around me. It was all very physical with a lot of grabbing and slapping as well. I was determined not to come too soon as I might not have another opportunity and the best way to guarantee another go at her would be not to! So I put in a good performance all the time circumnavigating her anus, slowly touching, slowly prodding. She encouraged this as well, grabbing my hand, pushing it closer, one finger into her pussy, and one into her arse. This continued until my middle finger was deep into her arse until I mounted her from the side. She seemed to enjoy this greatly and then I removed my finger to show I wasn't shy and liked my finger and slid it back in! All the while her arse was getting a little bit looser and a little bit wider and a little bit more in the zone so that something else could replace the finger.

You have to bear in mind at this point that she still had a black bra and black knickers on which was keeping me so aroused. It was now coming to the witching hour as you might call it. Would she take it or would she not? I was wearing a condom as I was having sex with her in the normal manner, but for the arse I thought I'd change. So I turned her over. She was spread, head down, stomach down, and I rammed my tongue into her pussy in the doggy position and then from her pussy I put my tongue into her arse, then my finger. Then I said, "Do you really want me, do you really want me here?" "Yes," she said… nothing more, which was surprising for such an intelligent girl. Clearly I had been given the green light now in respect of hygiene and the fact it was now or never. I took off the condom, put on a new one and slowly eased myself onto her. Now I thought I was going to hedge things in, but no! She said in the clearest Russian voice you could imagine, "Just put yourself in me, just put yourself in my arse, right now!" This was music to my ears and meant I didn't have to deal with that awkward 'are you in or not', that 'ooh, ah, slowly, is it in' moments, 'oh that hurts', 'slowly, faster'... you may know how women can be with anal sex.

So then with a little bit more saliva on me and in her I fucked her in her beautiful arse for the next ten, fifteen, twenty minutes, until I could take no more! I pulled myself out of her, her still in her beautiful black underwear and beautiful black ankle boots, and I came all over her tits and her pussy. But that wasn't good enough for her. Oh no! "Get back inside me," she said. Now, with the condom off which is probably ill-advised in these circumstances, I put my still erect cock back into her arse. Cum acting as a lubricant, she then fucked me so hard grinding on me so hard this girl was fucking like you could not imagine, this girl could move. Not all brains, not all beauty, but she could fuck as well; what a sexuality!

5 Blood sports

I was staying in this hotel whilst moving between places. I thought it would be easier than doing my own laundry but it was one of these apartment hotels where you get towels, sheets etc dropped off and there was no other housekeeping service. I was going to be staying there a week and London was quiet at the time, but in these times you have to take any port in a storm and that port was called Louise. I'd met her a few times before. She was a beautiful girl but, being flat-chested and with skinny arms, she wasn't really my type. However she moved well and had that look in her eye of a girl who has a mischievous sexuality. And, as is so often the case, this played out in a way you couldn't imagine. The hotel wasn't that great but I knew it was fine to take a girl back, so I took Louise back. She was drunk and drunk girls are fine but to go back with them you have to really fancy them. I didn't really fancy her but thought, fuck it and took her up anyway. We rolled about and then she announced when she was down to her underwear, "Hey, I've got my period." Lovely! Not only have I just wasted the last few drinks on you, sweetheart, but I've also waited half an hour for a taxi when I could have just ridden home on my bike parked around the corner.

So, not impressed, I said goodnight, rolled over,

light off! She was having none of that. The next minute her hands were around me and she was stroking, she was touching, and she was pressing her bloodied-up fanny against the side of my hips. What was I supposed to do? So I turned around and gave her a little bit of attention, a little bit of anus touching. She had nice little tits which kept me entertained for a while, but once again I didn't know where this was going so I turned over once more. She muttered a few words, tottered off to the toilet, then came back without her little tampon. So I thought, fine, ready for action, turned off all the lights, as you do in these situations when you don't fancy the girl. That way you can use your imagination and use whatever resources are available to you at that precise time. That was fine. I put in a half-decent performance, she was wet. I remember thinking, cool, she's turned on, she's wet which made the shag even better. Fortunately I'd bagged up as well. By this point it was 4 o'clock in the morning and I had to get up early for work. So she fell asleep until 7. I was feeling a bit restless, hot and sweaty. She was a little restless as well and kept fidgeting. I assumed she had to go to work early as well when she got up at 7 and off she went. But she was in a hurry which was strange. I pretended I was still asleep which is always the best way to be in these circumstances. Just get them out of the fucking door so you can get on with cleansing your soul.

Unfortunately, with this particular incident I had a lot more than my soul to cleanse. I rolled over still feeling hot, sweaty and a little flustered, pulled back the covers and jumped in shock as a massacre was revealed. Yes, Laura had her period and I thought she would be OK. She had said the same but this was nothing short of a lie. The place looked like Beirut in 1982 – no, worse than that – it looked like Vietnam in 1964. It was a bloody mess from the pillow to the sheet to the oversheet to the duvet. Everywhere, even on my white shirt, up the wall, everywhere. Anyway I packaged all the stuff up together in such a way that I could take it downstairs, leave it with the service people and they'd be none the wiser as when they take your dirty sheets they immediately give you new clean ones. Normally, under these circumstances, you can't be identified as to whose soiled sheets are whose, so are in the clear. I dropped the sheets off and the assistant was very helpful but a little too helpful. Rather than just taking the sheets and bundling them into the washbasket, he decided to look through them to see if there was anything wrong. Not a good idea! It was like that scene from 'Trainspotting'. He was pulling at the sheets, I was pulling at the sheets, but he pulled harder and next minute the sheets unfolded, and the bloody splattered mess was there for all to see. Brilliant! So I made a decision to scarper.

As I said things were a little dry in London at the time, but they were about to change. I met this cute little actress girl that I managed to pull, half-Chinese, half-Australian. Petite, beautiful, everything small but so tight. I took her home about two nights after the bloody incident. Now no problem this time – straight in, a good going over of her body, tight skin, perky little tits, great arse and she had that Asian thing whereby she really wanted to move her hips every way, shape and direction possible. She had a real appetite for sex just like any actress filled to the brim with insecurities and desperate to put in a good performance, which she did! Mine was pretty average but hey ho, I finished it off doggy style and came all over her back and hair and then fell asleep, as was the case before. She also left early the following morning seemingly having something more important to do. I leant over to get myself together and lo and behold what was there but a bloody patch. It was nothing on the chainsaw massacre, but there was a huge solid stain right at the top of my bed, not one you could disguise, but soaked right through to the mattress. Thankfully I managed to get the mattress scrubbed up as well as possible and got the sheets together again. However I was a little wary this time. Would I see the same assistant as before? I went down bracing myself for the embarrassment. Fortunately, as I looked around the corner, they had a different guy working, so I went up to give this guy the sheets. Frustratingly another customer steps out in front of me, so I wait in line tentatively. Then who comes from behind the partition but my little friend. He sees me, I see him! There is nothing I can do: I've got to give him the sheets again. Once again we go through the rigmarole of him seeing the sheets. I quickly leave them with him and get the hell out of there. Slightly embarrassing!

Now at this point I've done two girls in two days

both of them leaving a bloody mess, so I resigned myself that weekend to just taking it easy. No more girls, just in case the worse was to happen. Little did I know that two girls I had seen the previous week, one stripper, one actress, were out so I ended up in tow with them. Now I'd hoped to end up back at theirs but that wasn't possible as one of them had a boyfriend who was staying there. I sort of smelt there was some potential for a bit of action and also more than a scent of lesbianism between the two, but of course in these circumstances you are more than happy to be a bit of meat in a lady sandwich. I went home and had one of those awkward threesomes where they were kind of into each other but a little shy. One of them was a bit uncomfortable because of her boyfriend. It never really went the way I wanted it to; it was like the guide dog for the blind scenario where you can do this, but you can't do that. However I managed to have sex with one of them whilst fingering the other one. But I was concentrating on Angela, the one I was fucking, so much I forgot about Lydia. Angela was the more beautiful one and Lydia was just there to do the job which she did. This was all done under much drunkenness and not a lot of light. We all fell asleep in a big group, woke up in the morning and said our goodbyes. Lo and behold, the hat-trick had been scored, yes, the holy trinity was there for all to see. Not only was there a little blood on display, but one of the girls had got excited and left the worst skid mark I had ever seen. Stretching from my pillow halfway down the bed, not your usual type of skid mark but this had a yellow kind of tinge about it. So God only knows what I was going to do this time. I went downstairs and did a quick recce to make sure my little friend wasn't there, which thankfully he wasn't. So I headed down with these shit and blood splattered sheets having just scored the worst hat-trick you could imagine. Then I had to join the queue as a bunch of Japanese tourists had just turned up, but I decide to still wait as I couldn't be bothered to go back up to my room. Then who comes in starting his new shift but my little friend. He gives me the biggest smile, takes the sheets from me, doesn't even say anything. I say my goodbyes and I'm on way, mortified.

6 The sexy one

The first time you enter a strip club is kind of like

the first time you enter a casino, except multiply it. It's like the first time you go to a football match: you've got the lights, you've got the atmosphere, the noise and the anticipation. Now roll that into one and team it with sex.

My first time in a sex club was just off Soho. It was well known to a lot of businessmen and the odd celebrity and footballer. I went in there with about five guys all paid for by my rich mate. We'd all been offered a free dance, and I was excited to see the object of my affection for the evening. There were a lot of other girls in different shapes and sizes, but none had particularly grabbed me to the extent that I wanted to cash in my free dance just yet.

Finally, towards the end of the night, I caught the eye of this beautiful blonde girl, maybe Australian or South African or maybe an outside chance of being British. She was tanned and toned with fake tits, but good fake tits in keeping with the rest of her body. She had a tight waist and a beautiful curvy arse. She looked great, with high boots on and an ivory dress. Unfortunately, being one of the top girls in the place, she has been taken by a more financially astute group than ourselves. However, I managed to construct a scenario whereby I got one of my friends to distract the guys she was with so I could talk to her for a minute or so on the way to the toilet. I made it clear I liked her and she agreed that if she could she would come and do a dance for me. Sure enough, about half an hour later, I got my private dance. It was fantastic. Cassie, as she was called, was from the Gold Coast in Australia. She even had that matching golden coast tan. She teased me with her moves but she was being very sexy. I was trying to steer her away into something more normal, a normal conversation, and it became apparent that she was more than a little bit interested as she took that classic female step of asking my star sign. Would you believe it – not only did we have the same star sign but in fact shared the same birthday, so there I was in a strip club for my first time finally meeting someone who shared the same birthday, or at least she said she did. The guys laughed at this but I don't know. There was something in the girl's eyes that led me to believe she was a little bit interested. We swapped numbers sneakily and arranged to meet in a popular nightclub near by. An hour later all the other guys had gone home, but I didn't care. Cassie turned up with a cute friend of hers, Amy. We had a little chat, and got a bit drunk and went to some other nightclubs and got a little more drunk. I was nervous as this girl was a little bit of a handful and a little bit out there. It was getting close to decision time and the witching hour, so to speak. She didn't seem that keen to go home with me but at that point I was desperate and ready for action and this girl was really turning me on.

Her friend came to the rescue as she liked me so at least we could go on home for a couple of drinks. Cool! As soon as we got home her friend pretty much disappeared just leaving me and Cassie. Excellent! I was done with polite conversation and we made our way to the bedroom where she had a little dance to the music, shimmering her skirt up one leg at a time, looking back at me, and still completely in control. Almost self-consciously slipping back into stripper mode. With the boots and the dress she really looked the part. Finally she kicked her boots off and instructed me to get down to my underpants. She was in control and I was loving it! Then we kissed passionately and had a little roll around in the room that she had which was covered in trinkets. She was quite clearly into Buddhism or some other sort of spiritual religion. This was miles away from her night-time activity —far from spiritual. We made out and now she was on top of me; she sucked my dick with everything she had using her tongue, lips, even her ears, and she did it in the most wanton fashion! Fantastic! From there, now fully naked, she teased me sliding up and down and getting her pussy lips to tease the top of my erect cock. I just wanted to have her there and then. I couldn't take it anymore so I turned her around, lifted her and pushed myself in. It was fantastic, she was tight and with almost every push she contracted her pussy muscles, a true professional. Unbelievable! We probably went through three or four positions over the next fifteen minutes. She was getting that beautiful sex glow across her face. And, despite being pissed as a fart, I was putting on a half-decent performance. Fortunately for me under the circumstances this girl could come really easily. I was ready to come there and then. I was shattered, knackered, I'd just had one of the best nights of my life and I wanted to finish it off in a good fashion. She spun me around at the last minute. And she was licking up and down my shaft to my anus, my balls. I was just about to come, and she then lifted her mouth, obviously not a massive fan of the spunk. The first two spurts just shot out all over her, passed her head, then a further three which went over her head and all over the wall, which I thought wasn't good. She looked a little pissed off, looked at me, looked at the wall; in fact she looked really pissed off. She turned round and sauntered into the kitchen. It was only at that point that I looked over my shoulder and realised why. There on the wall was a picture of her mum and dad that she had spoken about in such glowing terms earlier in the evening. Unfortunately there were her mum and dad with cum dripping all down their faces; not good, then again probably better theirs than their daughter's. Still, one of the most uncomfortable moments of my life.

There is something about strippers that turns me on: their vulnerability, accessibility, but downright sexual dons as well. They may work in the industry but they carry their playtime home with them as well. Anyway I was lucky to get into a relationship with a London stripper; a fantastic, stormy, sexually intensive relationship. Fortunately she wasn't as nuts as most of them and we separated amicably, purely due to geographical circumstances. I had to leave the country for eight months and therefore we kept in touch. She came over and visited and we remained on good terms with the occasional bit of casual sex. Now, if you get on the right side of an alpha stripper she will introduce you to other stripper friends, and the next minute you can be with three, four, five strippers or more and hanging out with them, and God knows what this can lead to.

There was one night I'd just finished up with one of these girls, Olivia, a friend of one of my exes Julia whom I had been seeing earlier in the year. I also knew there was another girl, a friend of theirs who was also interested so things were looking good. We met up in a nightclub. That's the genius of meeting and dating strippers: you don't have to spunk hundreds and hundreds of quid just to get into some girl's fanny. With strippers, in normal circumstances, all you have to do is buy them a couple of drinks, have a laugh, treat them well, then I promise you'll have a lot more potential than if they were in their working environment. So anyway we went to a pretty seedy nightclub in central London, the kind of place where anything goes, kind of neither gay nor straight where people are just up for a good time, bohemian if you like. My kind of place, the girls' kind of place. We were sectioned off in the VIP area where we met a friend of ours, a Russian guy. Being a complete playboy fun-time Freddy, he had pockets packed full of drugs as well, so it was a little bit of indulgence; he did coke, I did pills, everyone was happy. We were also joined by another girl, a girl who I thought, at this particular point, I quite liked but wasn't too sure. Her name was Adjenta, so we had Adjenta, my ex Julia and Olivia who I had had a little thing about. So it was now three girls, one guy. Julia at this point starts to kiss the Russian boy. I didn't really care. I didn't have a particular crush on the three girls so I was happy to just let things run their course. It also became apparent that, although Adjenta was a little keen, she also had a liking for girls as well, so there was a lovely bit of sexual tension between Adjenta and Julia.

Now, just to paint the picture here, you have Julia

who is cute, sexy, kind of strong, a little bit too much testosterone as well, and nice fake tits. She is Brazilian, nice thick arse, really sweet girl as well and a kind of sexy husky voice. On the other side you have Lydia; she's nice, kind of cute, a little bit spiteful, you couldn't trust her as far as you could throw her, but obviously that adds a little to the bedroom as well. Finally, the last girl, Adjenta, who is kind of short, big fake tits that suited her thick arse, tanned with a sexy Hispanic face and this amazing tattoo. Now I'm not really one for tattoos but this was nice, stretching right down her back, a snake-like tattoo going perfectly into a nice little rump. Anyway the five of us got on like a house on fire. Julia and the Russian boy were getting on and the other two seemed to like me and showed a little interest in each other, so they were happy kissing.

It was getting a little too seedy for this nightclub so I suggested we go back to my little studio flat in Camden. We busted it over there and I sensed there was the possibility of a little action. In these situations the last thing you want to do is speed things along too heavily. The first thing you want to do, especially with one other guy, is make the girls feel relaxed and not try and force the issue. This is exactly what we did: I disappeared into the kitchen and made some drinks, leaving the Russian boy to do whatever he was doing with Julia, which was developing into more than heavy petting. But he was fucked so I'm not sure just how much performance he had in him potentially. Anyway I came back with the drinks but having only been away for ten minutes a pleasurable sight awaited me: not only were the Russki boy and Julia in their underwear petting heavily, but more importantly Adjenta and Lydia were kissing heavily. Already Adjenta was taking down Lydia's underwear which was nothing short of fantastic. I was really turned on; it was a great sight: my bed, in my little studio flat, three girls along with one guy, all swapping juices, saliva at this point, but soon to be other juices.

I had a look at the bed, looking for where I could be best utilised, so I was walking around the bed kind of like Alex Higgins used to do with a snooker table. One eye on one part, another looking over there. Now at this point Adjenta had just taken off Lydia's jeans to the extent that I could see her beautiful black G-string set amongst her tanned, tough, durable arse. I didn't hesitate. I went straight in there, sliding my tongue over her buttocks and straight into her pussy. There was a fantastic yelp, and also underneath her Adjenta let out a lovely squeal as my turning on of Lydia had turned her on in turn. A fantastic three-way, this threesome we were having didn't interfere with my Russki friend or Julia. But this was about to change.

Julia got up to make herself ready for a little bit of deeper action. Meanwhile, after over-partying too much, our Russki friend had passed out following too much coke and booze; he was dead flat out with a cock which was about as hard as a roll of rope, but there you are: one man's loss is another man's gain. And Julia soon came over to enjoy the action. She started sucking and playing with my ball sac as I had my tongue deep inside her friend. Adjenta tasted fantastic but you felt she got as much if not more joy from licking a girl's pussy than having her pussy licked by a boy. So, not one to be selfish, I allowed her to turn around and she and Julia started heavy kissing and before long they had their fingers inside each other's pussy. Lydia was lying there and she was getting some action also as Julia had gone straight for her pussy as well, allowing Adjenta to come around and put her tongue and fingers inside her. This was fantastic: all three girls linked by fingers and tongues, all turning each other on, all getting more and more hot. As I was waiting there, I could hear Julia muttering how hot this was and how turned on she was. She seemed the more likely candidate as Lydia still had issues with me as I'd fucked her only a few weeks before and hadn't pursued it. Adjenta was definitely enjoying the girls more than the boys so it was quite obvious at this point Julia was the best option.

I stuck my cock deep inside her and she let out an almighty scream and this was only helped as she had her tongue three inches deep inside Adjenta's pussy. Adjenta loved me fucking her, even taking her mind off the fact that Adjenta was smothering her friend with her beautiful labia; what a sight it was. Me with one leg over a rack of bodies fucking Julia hard, having a look and not seeing Julia's face as it was smothered by one of the best arses with the nicest tattoo I'd ever seen. All the while on the outskirts of this little three-way was little Lydia putting her arse onto Adjenta's face. It was the best; these girls didn't question taboos or ask what was morally correct; they just let their bodies do whatever the fuck they wanted to. My bed was great: it had this fantastic headboard so Lydia used it to the best advantage. With her two legs spread whilst balancing her arse on the headboard, she thrust her pussy back into Adjenta's face. Adjenta in turn thrust her pussy on top of Julia who was being fucked by me, who was really turned on and being smothered by her best friend; what a fantastic sight. I left the three girls to themselves whilst they all fingered and played with themselves. In the meantime I worked out how I was going to finish off this fantastic orgy. My poor Russki friend missed it all as he was snoozing, but that didn't take anything away from what was going on. I figured it was best actually if I fucked one of the birds and came in the other. Adjenta, however beautiful and sexy she was, clearly wasn't that fussed about boys, but wouldn't have any complaint as I had orchestrated this orgy. I finished off fucking Julia whilst I was fingering Lydia who was simultaneously licking Adjenta's pussy. This could only work for so long as it was such a fantastic scene. But it was becoming too much. I pulled out of Julia's beautiful tight pussy and came really hard all over that beautiful snake tattoo on Adjenta's back. She winced in the beginning but she didn't really care as she was too busy getting her pussy licked. A wonderful sight and a wonderful finish: the four of us and my soft-cocked Russki friend strewn over a big bed. Really, you couldn't buy that sort of entertainment.

7 Miami mischief

You have to love a warm climate. It brings out the best in people and gives a joie de vivre and heightened sexual awareness… OK, let's stop the pretence; it makes people horny.

Miami in February is a particularly good example of this. South Beach with its gorgeous Art Deco buildings and decent bars, clubs and beaches provides all the trappings of a good time. And yes, there are a lot of sexy models. In a small market like Miami you tend to get to know the girls pretty fast and it's a matter of luck which girls are in your agency at a particular time, but this time was resource rich.

Two of the best three girls were Barbara and Orly, the former Ukrainian and the latter American. They seemed quite bookish but that added to the intrigue. Barbara was twenty-five and Orly twenty and there seemed a strange connection between the two, a little bit of sexual tension, but then again that may just have been my fantasies getting the better of my reason.

The three of us met up for coffee a few times and had dinner together but it was hard to get onto anything that acted as a catalyst for flirtation. The other problem was that I fancied both of them but I knew that I couldn't really make a play for either as they were pretty close. Just as we were entering into the dreaded realms of the friendship zone, the weekend came around. I went out with a couple of mates and finally met the girls in a club. Both girls looked amazing: Barbara with tight jeans showing off her perfect ass and a white scoop top cut just above her nipples. Orly had a nice dress which disguised her perfect ten body. Orly was doing shots and it wasn't long before she was too wasted and I suggested we had better take her home. Barbara agreed and for the first time I could see a naughty glimmer in her eye – let the games begin, I thought.

With Orly out of contention I began giving Barbara a little ice-breaking massage. I knew we would have to look after Orly back at the apartment so I wanted to put my cards on the table. A few more kisses on the neck were given and happily taken and things were looking promising. Back at the apartment Barbara and I carried Orly up the stairs and dumped her limp body on the bed. It was a studio apartment with a thin rice-paper partition separating the two beds. It was all about Barbara now. I figured that most guys would go straight for that peachy bum of hers so I gave as much attention to her upper half as possible. Small though her tits were, she had fantastic nipples and they were either very sensitive or much ignored because she gave out little yelps of pleasure as I licked and teased. The heavy petting went on for an eternity but now I felt I had earned my right to devour the main course. I licked all over her stomach and slowly but firmly pulled down her jeans. She had a fantastic aroma down there and seemed freshly waxed. I licked her all over and flicked her round to have a closer inspection of THAT ass. It didn't disappoint. Just as I was about to put my tongue in her pussy from the reverse position I heard a voice say, "You guys are really turning me on." Orly was sitting up on the edge of her bed, not more than four metres away, not quite playing with herself but her hands were straddling her hips and upper thighs and I knew it could mean only one thing.

I quickly ushered her over to the sofa where Barbara immediately held her and gave her a kiss on the lips. She was still a little drunk but she really went for it. I gave her inner thighs a rub and simultaneously kissed her neck. Her hips moved with a wonderful natural sexy sway and while she seemed keener on Barbara than on me she still seemed to appreciate the attention that I was giving her.

With the dynamic as it was, I thought I should leave for a bit. So I lay on the bed taking it all in. An amazing sight seeing a horny twenty-year-old girl boss a horny twenty-five-year-old girl. Orly continued where I had started and gave Barbara some attention between her legs. There wasn't much rhythm to it but a lot of enthusiasm and some genuine lusty moans. The girls seemed genuinely into each other—these weren't just some lip-tick lesbians trying to get some more attention from boys. Orly ripped off her own dress revealing her top body. I had the back view but I adjusted my position so I could see her tits as well but added to the erotica was that Barbara could see me watching and gave me the occasional nod and wink of appreciation.

This was clearly not Orly's first girl-on-girl experience and she continued to dominate. She pulled Barbara onto her side and then took her pants off before wrapping her legs around her for the mother of all clit-banging sessions. It all made for wonderful viewing but I was beginning to get a little concerned about whether I would get back on the field of play. Orly was going crazy and seemed to be close to climax. Although not as loud, Barbara too seemed pretty aroused and I wasn't far behind.

Just when I thought my luck was out the exasperated Orly screamed and shuddered with pleasure before rolling over saying, "I'm too wasted. Mark, please take over." Without a moment's delay I was on Barbara. She had a really tight pussy but all Orly's work had made her wet and it was a struggle not to come too soon. Making the most of the couch and the fact that Orly was still on it I pulled Barbara up and pressed her against the wall for some hard fucking. I simply had to get the beautiful Orly back involved so I put Barbara back on the couch. I positioned her on her knees facing towards Orly. This was fantastic; I could fuck Barbara doggy-style and check out both her ass and Orly's über tits. Orly shuffled down the sofa and kissed Barbara strongly. This was all too much and as soon as Barbara screamed, "I'm coming, fuck, I'm coming" I slammed into her as hard as I could before falling like death on top of them both.

Music DJ

I can remember the very first time I met this guy: I was taking part in a celebrity football match. He loves a bit of football and always takes part regardless of what kind of night he has had the night before! So we are in the changing rooms and I've found myself making small talk and introducing myself when I recognise Mr P and he has a group of guys all looking at his laptop. Without a qualm he shouts hello and says, "Come over." He has loads of pictures of women fully nude and spreadeagled. His latest conquests, he laughs!

This guy leads a double life: one for his constant long-suffering girlfriend and the second for his rock and roll nightlife and naughty ways. He has two laptops, two phones, even two bank accounts. So I suppose he could be described as sneaky. Such a laugh, he's one of those guys who stands at the bar just getting round after round; he'll be the one running naked into the sea and, the fact that his life revolves around fun, why the hell not. In the past he has caused some serious abuse to his body whilst forging a superstar career as a music DJ in clubs around the world, top ten hits and sets to royalty in Ibiza. There isn't much he hasn't done. Enjoy some of his stories for Mr P is a little bit naughty!

I don't see myself as a ladies' man or one of those smarmy, slick creep types either. I'm a medium-built, average-looking man's man with very good manners. This is very important and I guess this bodes well for me as I haven't had too much trouble with the fairer sex in the past. I believe you need to think of them as equal; if not you're already losing. You see, I think of it like a game of chess…when you've found your opponent you need to be very patient. Moving your pieces around the table, taking your time, manipulating them, gently guiding them until eventually and unknowingly they move into the position you want them. Then the game goes out the window and I adopt the pincer movement, like they do in the army, and strike! This doesn't always go to plan, mind, no matter how good a chess player you are. There's always someone better out there, playing you at your own game, luring you in and waiting for you to drop your guard before adopting their own version of the pincer movement. They are crafty when they want to be, women. I've unknowingly engaged in games with 'chess masters' in my time and come unstuck. It's quite funny, really, and you have to see it as healthy competition. Ah, ladies. If only they realised how much control they really have over us…

1 Plop plop...

I was out with a couple of the boys for a night in town. We started a pub crawl and worked our way around most of the bars off Leicester Square. After six or seven drinks your mind starts thinking about birds obviously, and as I'm away from my bird for the night I have every intention of making the most of this. The plans start to get bird-centred and, as we are just a stone's throw away from the world's most famous lap dancing club, paid nudity seems the obvious choice. So we end up weaving our way to Spearmint Rhino on Tottenham Court Road. I love this place: as soon as you walk in there you feel like Hefner. So we have a few drinks, spend a few quid, and one by one the boys disperse until there's only me and Dave, a friend, left. The thing about strip clubs is that you think you'll only stay for a bit and before you know it you are reeled in. My mate Dave loves them; he likes to throw his money about so he's usually the last one to leave.

Anyway, I'd been chatting to one of the girls I know that works in there (she's actually a famous TV hairdresser's bird) and was also talking to her friend Tracy, a nice-looking girl but with a proper potty mouth, but that didn't matter as she had the best physique you'll ever see. I know most of these birds do too many drugs and too much extra-curricular overtime if you get my drift but I love them. Now this bird was filthy: she was saying how she could hardly walk cos her boyfriend fucked her in the backside the night before, blah blah... (you'll probably notice that there's a fair bit of back-door action in my stories... sorry about that... I just get a bit carried away when the mood takes me). It's always a good sign in my book if you get the dancer sitting with you talking as they then don't think of you as punters. You then have half a chance of getting hold of them. She was getting us free drinks, and popping off to the toilet to do lines of coke. It is amazing what goes on in this place; if you are in with the dancer you are in the 'club' if you like!

As the conversation continued, it got dirtier as did my imagination. She kept licking my ear hole and whispering that she wanted to suck my cock. Now she had a boyfriend and was still at work. I won't lie, I was starting to wonder if this was a stitch up. Well, we got more drunk and it was getting closer to closing time, and between us we decided it would be a good idea to go back to theirs after they'd finished work. Call it an after party. This is massively frowned upon by management so we had to sneak around the back and pile them into the cab and away we went!

Well, you can imagine what went on. I'm fucking her whilst my mate is piling into the other one. I'm loving the fact she has such a tight body, with a lovely arse and fake tits. I'm a dirty bastard and as you may know from reading this I'm not shy, but the long and short of it was she kept sticking her fingers up my arse. Now that's not really my bag to be honest but, as far as I can see, if I'm sticking things in her arse, I don't really have much of an argument when it comes to her putting a finger in mine. She was loving it, licking my rim, licking her fingers, properly filthy, but whatever floats her boat. Now I don't know if you've ever had anything up your arse but it's not the nicest feeling (actually, a tongue's quite nice, the other spearmint bird did that to me when I first met her as it goes). Having a finger in your arse makes you feel like you need to take a dump. So anyway, after some rolling around with this fuck bucket, I did my bit and we fucked off home. Great night, little tender, but some funny flashbacks and I had a big smile on my face as I'm getting into bed with my bird. Unbeknown to her that I'd been cock deep in a stripper two hours earlier, in fact she'd been finger deep in my arse, ha.

The next morning I'm up and about with only a few hours' sleep. You know how it works: you've gotta make out to the other half like it wasn't a heavy session. So I'm not sure if I need to take a shit or if I've just got a false fingernail lodged in my pipe. Something isn't feeling right so I head off to the toilet and I'm sitting on the crapper and waiting...waiting... Then 'plink... plink...' I'm thinking like that didn't really do the trick?! So I sit there a bit longer and finish the job and as I wipe my arse I notice something odd in the pan. No, not blood, or even a false nail, but two boiled sweets. The dirty bitch had been pushing boiled sweets up my arsehole! I laughed so hard but it was only fair as I had broken down her back door. My bird meanwhile was outside the bathroom wondering what I was laughing at!

I've actually got a friend that likes (or so he says) to have streaky bacon pushed up his arse and pulled out just as he's about to come! Anyway, that's another story. To this day whenever I see her celebrity boyfriend on TV I imagine him doing some late-night shopping at the newsstand for some mints just in case his missus is feeling fruity. What a great night. I saw her a few times after and, guess what, this time I was prepared!

2 Bum fun

Well, it started early as a night in the Big Smoke usually does. We all meet up in town for a bite to eat, Chinatown, nothing too heavy as we don't want to waste time. We end up staying here till our bellies are full and we're half-cut on rice wine. After a couple of hours we head down to the Denim Bar for a few where we meet some pals. It's a bit quiet to be honest and everyone's got itchy feet. "Off to the Kbar," someone shouts. It's always good to spend a few hours here as they often do model nights where all the girls come down for the free vodka and the club is happy as they are all pretty little things, and this night happened to be one of those. What a result! Let's go! Everyone grabs their bits and we hit the road. Twenty minutes in the cab and we are rolling into this heaving bar full of the beautiful people. I can tell this is going to be fun.

My friend's brother was a model and he was there with some skinny young ladies, just my type. He invited us over to enjoy the free booze and heaps of birds hovering near by. One of them happened to be his ex. Lovely looking, long dark hair and tanned skin and long, long legs. She caught my eye straightaway, not because I'd seen her before, she was just stunning. You have those moments when ya dick just twitches at the sight of a bird and she was amazing looking.

Anyway, enough about her for the moment. Me and my friend's brother were getting on it hard and fast, a bottle of Bud in one with a white wine chaser in the other. An absolutely stupid idea really, but seemed great at the time; as you know wine just fucks you up. He was telling me some stories about when they used to model out in Japan and all the nastiness they used to get up to. Sounds like the life to me. (Bit of a heads up to what these girls are really like!) So we're getting in the flow of things now; he's wrecked but still has the use of his mouth, OK. He tells me his friend runs Saturday nights at the Emporium on Kingly Street. So once again we are off to another venue. We round up some of the girls and a few of the lads and head over. The queue's massive, one of those horrid movie-type queues where the fit chicks get in and everyone else just waits in the rain. But it's not what you know but who, and the guy on the door gives us a nod; we walk to the front and straight in. He used to be a mate of mine on the scene when I used to work over in Ibiza.

Within minutes of getting in the girls are nagging me, asking me if I know anyone that can get them any drugs. Now I don't usually get involved in drugs; booze and birds are my fuel and there was plenty here; the Emporium's a great club for that. It has its fair share of minor celebs and footballers propping up the bar or in the corner or toilets powdering their nose so it doesn't take long before the picture-perfect beauties are all doing what they do and everyone's wrecked on one thing or another, stumbling about in an effort to dance.

Now by this time my mate's ex is getting friendly with me. Blame the booze or the drugs, I wasn't complaining. Jesus, she's beautiful. My mate (the model and her ex) was wrecked and slumped asleep in the corner which probably explains her over-friendliness to me now that he is out of the picture. We have a joke and a dance and move to the VIP area at the back of the club. It's dark and private and this is where it all starts to go wrong… or right, depending on which way you look at it. She's all over me, we're dancing, her hands are all over me and my cock's like stone. Man, she was hot. Then she puts her hand in her pocket and offers me a pill. "I've already taken two," she says, and slips it in my mouth. I'd have done anything for her right then, thinking with my cock as us men do, and washed it down with G&T when she slips her hand down into my jeans.

It's all getting too much by now; all I want to do is fuck this girl. So I drag her into the toilets; the attendants are fine if you cross their palm with silver… well, paper. We lock ourselves in a cubicle and get down to business. Right away she's down on her knees and feeds my cock straight down her throat. We were probably only in there five minutes fucking, well sucking in the toilets is never quite as much fun as you think it's going to be at the time. As we go back upstairs I can feel the E starting to kick in. I'd only done one, she'd done at least two and they'd given her the serious horn. So, with this information and a twitching cock, we leave the club and head to a hotel. It's getting light outside now and it'd been raining so the air smelt damp and dirty. As we get to my room we're ripping each other's clothes off. At last, I'm going to get to fuck her, bend her over and fuck that peach of a pussy. We must have spent hours fucking, I couldn't come and it wasn't through lack of trying, but she didn't care.

She went onto her hands and knees, pulled her long sexy index finger from her mouth and slid it into her arse; that was it. I knelt behind her and started to wind it in. I fucked the shit out of that tight little arse for what felt like hours! Doggy style, on her side, on her back with her legs up by her ears, both ankles in my left hand like I'm stuffing a turkey with a pork sword. Her arse took a complete pounding as I fucked it, not once going near her pussy. I'd only just met this bird!

Turns out I literally did fuck the shit out of her cos when I wake up about lunchtime the room fucking stinks.

The bed is full of shit, it's all over the pillowcases, the sheets, me! The poor girl, not so beautiful in the morning carnage. Meanwhile she is fast asleep in it. Turns out (so the doctor told her) that the drugs mixed with some serious anal don't do the ass any favours. Basically her backside had gone baggy and forgotten how to tighten up again! I'd like to think it's down to my massive cock. As you can imagine she was in bits when she woke up. It was actually quite funny, we rolled the sheets up and threw them out the window, filled her drawers with bog roll and off she went on her merry way.

I spoke to her soon after. She was cool, after explaining what happened to her doc (with a very red face, and arse). He just gave her some tablets and she was good to fuck another day, but I'll never forget the smell of that stinking hotel room. She was very, very, very fit, but my mate never did find out!

3 Queer night out

This is a strange story, so bear with me. I piss myself when I think of it and although I've got so many dirty deviant nights out sometimes things can go wrong but you've just got to roll with the punches, I guess. When I'm not chilling out at home, I'm either abroad, in Brighton or out in London. This one time I decided to meet up with some mates for a few down in Brighton. I'd not seen a couple of my mates from Brighton for a while so I made the call. After we'd had a few and a little crawl along the sea front we thought let's head back into London, so we jumped on the train into London Victoria for about mid-afternoon. It's good to start early as the night is far too short otherwise. After spending most of the day drinking in Covent Garden, checking out girls and watching the world pass by washed down by cold Coronas, me and my mates decided to hook up with another friend.

It was this friend's birthday and we'd been meaning to hook up for a while. He's a world championship boxer and was having a big private party at Café de Paris in Leicester Square. It's a lovely club, full of character as it used to be a theatre. He's also a good-looking boy with a lot of chat so we knew it would be full of panty. It was still pretty early so we head across the road and into Soho to see who's about, the usual mix of faces for a Saturday night.

With the usual full roads and people drinking in bars, we weave through a few streets and my friend taps on the door of what looks like a normal apartment flat in Soho as if it's an old friend's house. In he goes. As he's asked us to wait outside we're more than a little intrigued. An hour passes, we're sitting in the bar opposite when he's led out by two beautiful young ladies, a big smug grin on his face. "Come on then, let's hit Café de Paris," he says with a wink. It was literally a knocking shop and he's picked up a couple of sorts for the night.

We turn up at the door and go straight in. I'm not having this, I've got to get myself some fit crumpet so I take a stroll round. I was right: there's already plenty of hot chicks about. I start chatting to a few and keep pissing myself looking across at my mate looking like he's Hugh Hefner.

I can see my mate at the bar with his two hookers so I stroll over and we start smashing the Sambucas back thick and fast. The girls go for a walk and within seconds we're joined by the guy whose party it is. He's got a bottle of vodka in an ice bucket and a tray full of Red Bull. We walk over to his table, crumpet all over the place wearing not very much at all, things are looking good.

The next few hours are a bit of a blur: vodka, Sambuca, gin, more Sambuca… lots more Sambuca... I can't remember much. I can't remember leaving the club but I can remember walking for ages. I felt like I'd been walking for hours. I was an absolute wreck. I honestly believed I'd walked to Brixton… the area was proper rough. I eventually managed to flag myself a cab. You know when your sooo pissed that you can't even read the numbers on your phone, you can't for your life type a number or a text. Well, that was me. I couldn't contact anyone or even use my hands to make a call.

I remember rambling on for ages while my driver was driving me around. I think I managed to describe the hotel we'd booked for the debauched evening as we pulled up at the Park Lane Hilton. I'm working on mental clues and flashbacks here as I really can't remember much after leaving the club. I fall into bed and pass out.

About six in the morning I wake up in what seems like a strange place in a strange bed. As my eyes are adjusting I notice there's this guy on his knees at the end of my bed, looking at me with his cock in his hands! I kid you not, I absolutely shit myself! I leapt, pissed as a fart, out of bed, grabbed the cunt round the neck and threw him off the bed. The guy was screaming like a girl being raped! All of a sudden the door smashes open. In runs my mate, cigar in his mouth and a chick in a bikini and fur coat on each arm. There's me in my pants with morning glory and a naked crying Irish man lying at the bottom of my bed. My mate was pissing himself. After a few minutes it all calmed down and the Irish guy explains that apparently I jumped in the poor sod's taxi while I was stumbling around London. After spending two hours in a cab with me he thought he'd pulled and followed me up to my room when we got back to the hotel. I really didn't care what was going on around me. I was totally switched into 'emergency get-home mode' and was made up that we even found the hotel! I can only imagine what was going on whilst I was passed out. Luckily I woke up when I did or I might have had a salty baptism.

My mate and his chicks were laughing out loud as I sent him packing. After a few hours' sleep we had to get out of the room so I had a shower and cleaned up the room. For the life of me I couldn't find my wallet or my watch. Looks like I paid for my private gay sex show in one way or another, ha ha! The worst thing is that every one of my mates knows about this and more often than not it's brought up every time I'm smashed. It's a bit out there but one of the funniest most embarrassing experiences which I thought I'd share!

4 The clap

I know this lovely looking Irish girl. I'd been trying to get in her drawers for as long as I could remember. It was dawning on me that I was almost close to nailing her so me and a pal go out for a drink. We'd arranged to hook up with her and her mate so we head to their neck of the woods (knowing that with a stroke of luck we'd head back to theirs after). Little tip here, if you're meeting a girl for a night, when you think it could develop, meet near theirs as they feel safer going home there than to yours!

It started off gently but these girls were up for it and we all know that the Irish can throw the booze down their necks but this girl was in a different league. She wasn't a big girl by any means but loved a drink, and was always up for a night out. We were doing some serious boozing; my mate and the other girl were trying hard to keep up but we had set a serious pace. It's all going to plan, she's loving my jokes, she's flirting and it's going well but as the night goes on it all starts to gets a bit messy. Then those legendary words come out of her mouth, the words I'd been waiting to hear: "Why don't you two come back to ours for a few more cheeky drinks?" Oh go on then, you talked me into it!

We head back to their place in Islington for a few more. I know drinks were poured but I don't remember drinking, only flirting my arse off. So a bit of flirting later and I ask for a tour which leads to her room and me and Irish hit the sack. I'm a sucker for an accent so my cock was like a piece of oak the moment we entered her house! We had a good old-fashioned session. She had typical fair skin with little tits but I didn't care – I was finally fucking her! She wouldn't let me fuck her ass though, not through lack of trying, I might add.

The next morning we were on our way. My mate wasn't too happy after spending the night alone on the couch. Job done, I just got on with my life, bit of grafting on other bird, nothing special. Anyway, a couple of weeks later, I get this text. As I read it I noticed it wasn't meant for me. Irish had meant to send it to her friend (although I still think she'd planned it this way to make it easier for her to tell me). It read something along the lines of this: 'I've liked him for ages and we had a lovely night together the other week, but I've only just got my test results back and I'm worried I've given it to him. What shall I do? I don't know how to tell him!' Well, I shit it! I mean I'd been living with my bird for a couple of years and I couldn't remember if I'd fucked her since the Irish. I got on the blower and she explained that she had had the test before we hooked up but only just got the results. She had chlamydia. What is wrong with her? Why the fuck didn't she tell me? Not to worry, now I needed to sort this. OK, I needed a plan.

My brain went into overdrive so I went to the GUM clinic and got tested. They told me I'd get my results in a week but gave me a course of antibiotics anyway, just in case. That was me taken care of but what about my bird? I went back into the clinic and said I'd left my tablets in the waiting room by accident, so he gave me another box. Phase 1 complete. This is so wrong but what was I to do? I then went to the chemist and had a nose around the pills and tablets. I was after a specific type of capsule, one I could open and reclose. You'll understand why in a minute.

One box of branded cold and flu tablets, £2.99. I spent an hour sitting in my car emptying the capsules out and filling them with the clap tablets. Now I have a week's course of cold and flu tablets in a small brown pill bottle. Phase 2 complete. I now had to find a way to get my girlfriend to take them.

When she's had a drink she gets a terrible hangover. Lovely, I took her out, got her drunk… really drunk… then I waited... The next day, sure enough, she was complaining about her head, her back, blah, blah, blah… "Oh, you've got dehydration, I've read all about it… I've got an idea, my friend works in the chemist, I'll get him to get you these new anti-dehydration tablets, they'll sort you right out." I nipped out for ten minutes, well, kept the car running and took them out of the glove box. I came back with the tablets and said, "He said take two per day for a week and it'll sort out your dehydration!"

That was that… easy. Phase 3 complete and she was none the wiser. A few days later I got my results back and it turns out I was as clean as a whistle. Little does my bird know she had a course of antibiotics. Tell ya what, that was close. All that for nothing. I suppose it pays to cover your ass.

5 Threesome

Ah, this is one of my favourite experiences, made all the better by the fact it was a threesome…

what fond memories. Well, we're all getting ready for our flight back from Barbados, sitting in the airport cracking on with a few beers. It's probably a bit too early but the holiday doesn't stop till you get home and there is nothing more depressing than the flight home. We knock a couple back and our flight for London is announced. We finish our drinks and head down to the boarding gate and join the queue to board the plane. I must admit I'm looking good: I'm tanned, got some good money in my back pocket from some sets I did out there. Life is good; often, when you feel like this, life goes your way!

Waiting to go through there was this group of Geordie girls about twenty feet in front of us, late teens, early twenties, they look like air hostesses. As we sat down I noticed the girls were sitting in a group to the right of us. All bar one of them. She'd obviously come later and had got separated from the group. Her seat happened to be right in between me and my mate. It almost seemed like one of those nature programmes where the one zebra gets separated from the group and ends up surrounded by hungry lions. Prey on the defenceless one, easy pickings. She was all prim and proper at the beginning, polite and friendly. But it's a long flight and we were fairly lit up from the booze. Two bottles of bubbly and a few hours later and she's a different person! In all fairness the whole group were good fun but this one had turned into a monster! She was telling us her fantasies and how she wanted to fuck someone in the ass with a strap on, and how she's got a thing for sticking her tongue up her fella's arse. Mmm... She sounded like an interesting character.

When we landed we all swapped numbers and we were on our way, still intrigued by what she had said on the flight. I hooked up with this bird a few times after we got back but nothing really happened. I thought I'd try the hard-to-get technique for a change, see if it actually worked, and it seemed to do the trick as she was all over the texts and calling on my secret second phone. It was my birthday and we all arranged a night out at a couple of clubs in town. We'd start off at 'The Player'. It's a small bar, members only; you walk downstairs into a wide low-ceilinged room. The small gay guy that runs the night is friendly with us as one of my mates had done some work for him in the past. He takes us to the bar and starts us on the absinthe. They do all this fancy shit with brown sugar and fire and stuff, like you see in the movies. The first couple get you completely off your tits so it doesn't take long to get in the mood. After about an hour or so we'd had enough so we head to Brown's where we meet up with the rest of the guys and a couple of the Geordie girls we'd met in the airport and their pals. We're all having a laugh and the stories are flowing and, as the night goes on, the one with the fetish (we'll call her Fetish) seems to be focusing all her attention on me.

I'm more than happy to be chatted up by a fit young blond with massive tits so it was going down rather well. Also, the more I plied her with alcohol the friendlier she got, hinting that I go back with her, exactly as I had planned whilst all the time I'm playing hard to get. In the end she actually suggests we go back to hers so her and her friend can give me my birthday present. Did I hear that right?! Well, how could I refuse that, so I drank up and we were off. It was my birthday after all.

So the three of us head back to hers, pretty much straight to her bedroom. I'm sitting at the end of the bed and they start kissing, just doing a show for me. I knew I was going to enjoy this. Fetish started by kissing her friend's neck, working her way down her friend's shoulders. She slipped her hand round the front and into her top always looking into my eyes knowing it was getting me going. It was killing me; sitting there I needed to get involved. I whipped my clobber off and jumped on the bed but Fetish was having none of it. She kept pushing me back. "It's not your turn yet," she said to me. "Just lie at the end of the bed, watching and waiting."

Fetish by this time has her friend on her back. She's smiling at me while she undoes her top. Fetish is between her legs easing her skirt up around her waist, and as she starts to pull down her little panties I'm struggling to contain myself. I've got my cock in my hand by now wanking, just watching Fetish with her tongue in her friend's pussy. They both look amazing together. I could see Fetish fingering her while she licked her clit. I'm gagging for it, then she stops for a second, turns to me and calls me on. All pissed up

I'm on her like a shot, trying every position I can think of, making a few new ones up as I go. We fuck for ages, first Fetish, then her mate. She reaches behind, takes my cock and shoves it in her arse. Pure fantasy stuff, I'm fucking Fetish in the arse while she fingers her best mate. I don't stand a chance of coming as I'm too drunk but that's not going to stop me making the most of this!

Eventually I get her friend in front of me playing with her pussy; Fetish is behind me with her tongue in my arse. I reach down the side of her bed and grab this can of deodorant. Using it as a dildo I'm fucking this bird with it while the other one's behind me. Then the girl grabs my arm. "The lid's in me!" she says. "The lid's come off the can." I'd forgotten it was even a can I was using, we were all so 'in the moment'. The lid was properly wedged in her pussy, really in deep. I could touch it but it had moved round and now I couldn't get a grip on the domed lid. Ha, ha, it's terrible really but by now the moment was well and truly gone. For the next ten minutes she had a naked man and a naked woman sitting between her legs rummaging around her pussy like we were looking for small change! In all fairness, when we eventually got it out, she was as good as gold. Sadly the moment was over and we all hit the sack and got some sleep. A very horny experience with the funniest outcome I could ever imagine.

6 Christmas stuffing

This is one of those things that happens and you'd never think for a million years that a day like this exists, purely because it's so out there! It's Christmas morning and as usual at this time of the year I wake up at my bird's parents' house. All's good, we have our quick morning fuck to ease the morning glory, then breakfast: smoked salmon and scrambled eggs with champers. If it's good enough for Prince Charles, it's good enough for me. Anyway, I've been getting texts from these two birds all of the previous night as we'd gone out for a few on Christmas Eve. One was a pretty Italian-looking thing I'd met a few months before in London, dark, a PA for some law firm, loved tight tops which showed off her big old tits, even had a good bum to be fair. Sadly she had a boyfriend which meant I hadn't fucked her yet but I knew she was keen judging by the messages she was sending me. The other was a pretty ex of mine from a few years back who I would pump every now and again, fit as fuck. Not the best face but so dirty, I used to love fucking her.

One of the things I've noticed as you get older is you find less and less to do on a Christmas morning which is at all thrilling beyond opening presents and, no disrespect to my in-laws, but I'm a little bored. It's only about 10.30am and I've got the raging horn as usual already so, as I lie there on the sofa phone in hand, I start to plan to my morning out, texting these birds. Everyone is opening presents, eating chocolate, and I'm smiling along whilst texting the dirtiest messages to these birds. They've both taken the bait, I'm on my way.

I tell the other half that I've got to pop to my mum's to wish her a happy Christmas, and that she doesn't need to come. I'm on my way. By 10.50am I'm at my ex's house, she opens the door with fuck all on bar some kinky undies with some quick release ribbons on the sides. I can't resist, I drop to my knees in her hallway, pull the ribbon out with my teeth so the knickers drop to the floor. Her little landing strip is inches from my nose so I can smell her sweet pussy. I slowly ease her lips open with my tongue, into her warm wet pussy… I love eating pussy… she lifts her left leg over my shoulder, takes my head in her hands and forces my tongue deep into her. After she'd had her fill of me she took me by the hand into her bedroom and in seconds my jeans are round my ankles and I'm so far down her throat her eyes are watering. (Got to keep an eye on the time, I'm only supposed to be down the road.) I take her onto her bed, bend her over and slip it in her. (Got to get out of here really.) I fuck the shit out of her for about ten minutes, doggy with my thumb in her ass for good measure, make my excuses and bust a move. In and out in about twenty minutes, not bad, although I did feel a little harsh leaving my ex alone after fucking her on Christmas Day. Oh well.

On my way back the Italian chick texts me. I don't know why but I feel like I've got something to prove. I need more pussy. It's become a challenge now! 11.50am, I turn up at the Italian's house. Pretty little thing, sexy and dirty. Always a bonus, her mum and dad are in the front room but she knows the score and leads me in. Within minutes I'm doing her doggy in her bedroom. I'm kneeling behind her watching my hard cock going in and out of her tight little pussy, spreading her arse as I go. She's got a lovely arse, nice and wide. I check my watch: 12.15. (Got to be back before one really.) So I'm pumping hard and fast, slapping her arse like a porn star when, in a lapse of concentration I accidentally slip out and then back into her backside! Fucking hell, I've never felt such pain. There's blood pissing all over the place. I've split my 'banjo string' from the base of my helmet!

So there I am, 12.20, Christmas Day, kneeling down with my cock in my hands, covered in claret with some Italian bird that looks like she's been stabbed, on her hands and knees in front of me. Things really can't get any worse, or so I thought, when in walks in her mum. She'd been in the other room watching Christmas TV. She was sooo embarrassed, and rather shocked too, I guess. Certainly as I wasn't her daughter's boyfriend! But I was thinking about me and my bloody cock. Anyway, what do you do! Who cares, not my problem! With only a few minutes to get out of there before it all kicked off, I desperately needed some bandages but there was nothing to hand. So I wrapped my cock in a sock and cling film from the kitchen on the way out and got the fuck out of there leaving her to explain.

Well, I was back at the in-laws by 12.50, opening presents and eating dinner like nothing was wrong, except for the fact that I had a swollen cock in a bloody sock covered in cling film between my legs. Flinching in agony and unable to tell anyone or get out of the house, I had to deal with the agony all alone. That was enough sex for me for a few days!

7 Fire beard

Everyone's got a fire beard story. As you read on you will understand what I mean. A few years ago just before I moved out of my parent's home I was going through a stage where me and my mates would have some place to go every night of the week, depending on whether or not I was working at some club or not. That was when I didn't get hung-over and I could go to work after an hour's sleep having been partying all day. Anyway there were these girls that we used to knock about. Nice enough, I guess they were a couple of slags really but that's fine by me as they all liked a drink and would always be up for a pump. Great for practising your new moves on and no-strings-attached sex is never a bad thing. It probably helped that they would let you come over at all hours and get hold of them.

It was one of those standard nights: me and a group of mates were all out on the piss. I think there'd been some football on so we'd been out all day and were boozing hard. As the evening went on we decided we'd go to this club in town. The booze was flowing hard and I was having trouble keeping on my feet by this time. Just before I was going to knock it on the head, this bird came over to me with a drink. It was one of the group of girls we used to knock about with but I'd never met her. That said, never one to turn down a drink, we propped the bar up a little longer and she was all over me. Average height, tight jeans, a loose top, she didn't look all bad. I didn't really mind, I must admit. We were doing some gentle kissing at the bar and I had my hand resting on her bum and slightly under the arse cheek, I could tell she was up for anything that evening.

One of my mates had already snuck off with her mate, which obviously left me alone with her so I thought I might as well do the honourable thing and show her how it's done. So we grab our coats from the cloakroom and head back to her place for a few drinks. It felt a lot later than it actually was at this point as I'd been drinking for about twelve hours but it was only about 1am. We get to hers and crack open a bottle of vodka. I'm so spasticated with booze by now I can hardly see. We throw a few drinks down us then she drags me to her bedroom and down to business.

Now normally, from what I'd heard, this girl wasn't shy but for some reason she wasn't going over as easily as I'd been told she would. She had been all over me earlier but now was playing a little hard to get. Don't you just hate that. At least she was more than happy to suck my booze-fuelled semi but she didn't seem to want to get her kit off. At this time I was more than happy to just lie back and have her suck my cock and lick my nuts but as it went on I noticed the blood started flowing as it should and it wasn't long before I was hard like a tree trunk. It was easy getting her in the sack but I spent fucking ages trying to get my nuts in. She was having none of it. I was getting more and more aroused and she was breathing so heavily I thought, fuck this. I just kneeled between her legs and started throwing one off. I was wanking myself crazy, I really didn't want to waste this fucking great stiffy I had. You boys know what it's like, this must have been all too much for her.

She turned out the lights, grabbed my head, laid back, pulled her knickers to the side and pushed my face between her legs. I'm a sucker for giving head. I was eating her out for ages, she was so smooth down there. As she got wetter she climbed on top of me and started grinding her pussy on my face. Ha, I'm lying on my back, a slag on my face and cock in my hand. I like to think I'm pretty good at this and remember thinking, she's really turned on. So wet. I'm obviously doing all the right things. But then I noticed something wasn't right. It almost tasted like I had a mouthful of rusty nails. I think I'd cut my mouth somehow. Ah, fuck it, I whip my clothes off and flip her on to her back. I've got her legs pinned up so her knees are by her ears and she doesn't care any more, she needs some cock action! I take my cock and feed it into her, I'm nailing her good and deep. She starts moaning that she's about to come, I tell her I want to see her face as she's coming. I reach to the sideboard and turn on the lamp and all I can see is the look of horror on this bird's face.

I look down and there's claret everywhere! All over my face, up my arms, all over her legs, the bed, the lot. It looked like I'd fucking killed her! "I think I'm on my period," she says! Ha, ha, I started gagging, I've got to get outta here! I legged it to the bathroom, cleaned myself up as quickly as I can, put my clothes on and busted a move. When I got in my mum was up getting ready for work. I stroll in like it's all good, whip my coat off and start making a coffee. Within seconds my mum's laughing, absolutely pissing herself. She points at my white T-shirt and there's a big red arse like one of those Rorscharch pictures on the chest. I could only bite the bullet and explain. Lucky for me, she's pretty cool.

The Drummer

I've known him for years, back when he was in a band and even now, as someone who produces big music extravaganzas, our paths always cross. In his phone book he has all these numbers of rock stars, movie stars; he's met them all and worked with some of the best. The best thing is, as a musician, a lot of his life is fairly open. He has enough regular work to pay the bills and then some! But it's the freedom which I think makes him so unique. He does so many different types of jobs in so many different countries that he can't help but be interesting to women.

The thing about Mr F is that he has a great banter, he always has the last line and loves a drink, a fag and some chat with his mates. A generous guy to the end and one of the best listeners you will ever meet, although slightly deaf from years of aural abuse. The fantastic thing about being a drummer is you aren't in the limelight but you are: no one really knows who you are but you have access to everything a rock star does. He lives a charmed life and the fact is that he is genuinely interested by other people; ladies love that. He knows it and exploits it to his maximum. I've watched him and whilst everyone is smashed he'll be grafting some young thing in the corner. Very old school and very good fun.

Being a drummer in a band can be an open licence to grab a lot of pussy and, trust me, I have more than abused/taken advantage of it at every given opportunity at gigs but normally I use that hook when I'm out on the town just for a challenge...me, I'm just a normal-looking bloke with loads of cheeky chat and a quirky job...but fuck me, have I nailed into some plumber's tool bag in my time. A very high percentage of birds can be incredibly gullible and will believe any old bullshit story. My secret is to make them laugh and chuck the first mental story into them I can muster up on the spot. (One of my favourite ones is telling them I am a ghostwriter for soft porn novels and I am doing research. It's worked before, trust me…try it). This is to get them interested in staying for more alcohol which always helps the mission of peeling the panties off and accomplishing it with more ease. Combine that with risky shock humour and, before you know it, their little silk triangles have dropped down on the floor and they are being nailed long and hard to the nearest mattress. Mind you, one of the best skills to be learned is how to get them or yourself out of the door without incident and letting them believe they will be seeing you again...mmmm maybe, sometimes, but most of the time I don't fucking think so, girls. Sorry, but once we get what we want it's usually bye-bye and straight on the phone to the mates to tell the tale. It will take a really special chick to make me pick curtains...maybe one day!! I do always keep in mind that they hold the ultimate power: they have to be the willing receivers of my fleshy drumstick. So it's up to us, boys, to do all the convincing. Sometimes it's not always the case and you latch on to some wild ones as you will read...but, fuck me, it's a lot of fun doing all the groundwork and eventually getting the moist prize behind the cloth. I hope you enjoy my London town adventures. Trust me, that's just one city of stories. How much time have you got for the rest of my depraved goings-on? Enjoy and hang on to your wives, daughters and girlfriends. Remember, I'm always out on the prowl.

1 Nicole

I'm out on the smash with the boys in the West End. It's a lovely warm night, the sky is clear and the vibe in town is good. You know, sometimes everything just feels right and in yourself you know things will fall into place. It was one of those evenings: the usual thing with the guys – beers, curry and find more drink. After the rugby, we're all in this bar in Soho laughing and drinking away and, for a change, not on the pussy prowl, just enjoying each other's company. Each one of us is trying to be the king of humour at every available moment. The crown was getting passed around big time. The banter was rife and this became a magnet to everyone around us...especially the ladies. Gentlemen, laughter is the key to the removal of the underwear!! A group of girls had latched onto us, enjoying the flowing laughter and drinks. One of them was, for want of a better description, like a young slim version of Nigella Lawson: very dark hair, lovely tits, almost Greek-looking. You know the kind: horny as fuck. I made a beeline for her and started chatting. It turns out she grew up in the same area as me, albeit she was ten years younger, (I didn't tell her that of course), so we had some common talking ground to start with. It turns out she is training to be a lawyer and has a boyfriend who is in the army and is away all the time. So it's decision time for me: do I work hard and try and pull her or just be nice and leave her the fuck alone? Fuck it, I'm half pissed, full of bravado as usual, and decide to pursue this dark beauty. I decide that the not-try-anything-play-it-cool approach is in order here, while plying her with as much alcohol as possible. I got on with her really well, made her laugh and started to ask about 'how she copes with boyfriend being away'. The next is a shocker: she says, "I just fuck who I like while he is away, no strings just sex, as I love my boyfriend but just need to fuck sometimes." I had to take a moment to compose myself here. What a fucking sucker punch that was...fuuuck. I of course ask if she would like to fuck me tonight. Her reply, and this gets better: "Yes but I want you to bring your mate over there as well so I can have the both of you together."

Johnny is an old pal of mine, got a sweet little bird for a girlfriend, but still sticks his dick in anything. I swear he would fuck a packet of liver if it looked at him nicely, dirty twat that he is. I call him over and introduce Nicole. I can see he likes what he sees. I whisper into Johnny's ear about her proposal. I am guessing here but, if anyone was watching his face as I explained the offer, it would have been a fucking brilliant changing picture. Now we hatch our escape, bearing in mind she is with her mates and we are with ours. Even though ours wouldn't give a fuck hers might so we need to leave discreetly. I suggest that she makes her excuses, leaves and walks around the corner to get a cab and tell it to hold on for us. A few minutes later Johnny and I just disappeared out of there without saying a word, knowing full well whatever goes on tonight will be discussed in detail over some beers with the guys (or even in a fucking book!!).

Nicole is waiting in the cab as promised and in we both pile. "Right, where to?" asks the cabbie. Nicole, bold as brass, gives him an address in South Kensington. She announces, "It's one of my dad's places he lets me use while I live in town." Turns out Daddy is minted, massive property guy. The journey to her place was a laugh and she sat between the two of us on the back seat making a fuss of both of us. I managed to slip my hand under her little dress and tease her pussy while we drove along just to check if she is for real. No resistance so onward us soldiers of the pussy must proceed into battle. We arrive at her place, pay the cabbie and in we go up to this penthouse apartment which is to fucking die for. It's an awesome place. Nicole takes charge as soon as we get in. "Sit down, boys, help yourself to drinks. I will be back in a moment." Johnny and I poured out a large whisky each and sat smiling at each other waiting. Nicole came through wearing the full gear: stockings, suspenders, sexy little basque and high heels. She walked over to me, took a sip of my drink, knelt down and snagged my face off while unzipping my trousers and pulling out my hard cock. As soon as it was out she took it down her throat...the lot, deep as she could...fuck. By now Johnny is half naked and preparing to drop his trousers. The cunt winks at me as he penguins with his cock out up behind her. He decides to lick her pussy from behind as she is blowing me...fuck Johnny, but as far as I could make out Nicole and I were in heaven. Johnny by now is lying on the floor licking her cunt with his head poking through her legs, sliding forward slightly and looking up occasionally like a fucking car mechanic at me and winking at me again (I would kill the bell end later for trying to make me laugh). Nicole takes out my cock and stands up, off the mechanic! She turns around and sits down on my cock, shoving it right up inside her. She had the hottest pussy I have ever had the pleasure of putting my dick inside. Johnny boy by now has stood up and she is wanking him off while he is groping both her sexy pert tits which he had popped out of the underwear she still had on. She is bobbing up and down fucking herself on my cock. I ripped away the panties she had on and by now Johnny has shot all over her tits. Thankfully none came my way. Nothing more horrible than another man's spunk on you…fuck that. She now has one hand on her pussy flicking her clit and the other rubbing Johnny boy's cum all into her tits...I am getting close to bolting. She knows her stuff and, as she sensed my pending explosion, she fucked down on my hard-on as I shot my load inside her roasting hot cunt. She timed her own coming right with mine. I fucking love that feeling of shooting up a bird as they are coming on you. It's top of the tree. Johnny and I, after recovering from bolting our loads, (you know us blokes we all talk like we want to fuck five or six times, that is until we bolt the first lot), anyways we abuse Nicole from all angles for the next few hours to come. She was a dirty bitch. I remember at one point her wanking both of us into her mouth and swallowing our jizz. She was porn star material, not lawyer!! Johnny left in the small hours but I couldn't be arsed and stayed the night. Nicole woke me up with tea for us both. She drank some, held it in her mouth before swallowing, then sucked my cock off with her red-hot mouth. Try it…it's fucking brilliant. Nicole was an awesome sexual experience. I never saw her again nor did we exchange numbers. I guess that's her way. She told us that. Who cares, a good time was had by all, and Johnny took great pleasure in holding court in the boozer telling the tale to the lads.

2 Carnage

It's amazing when what seems like a normal evening ahead can turn unexpectedly into sordid carnage, seediness and all that comes with it. It must be mixing with like-minded people. Anything can happen.

So I get a call from a good pal. "Mate, pick you up around 8pm. We're going out drinking in London, not telling you where but you'll enjoy it." So big T picks me up in his flash motor driven by his quiet but knowing driver Bill and off we go. Big T (that's all I'm telling you about him) has this devilish look in his eyes when the fucker is up to something. He is a great bloke but also slightly unhinged, awesome. We meet three more of the lads, have a few drinks in an East London trendy wine bar bantering and perving at the young sluts in their office work clothes on their after-work drinks. And then off we go to this private members' club (location has to remain top secret…sorry). It's one of those places that you just would not know it's there: just a normal door on a normal street. We get inside, dump our coats and go into this small but strangely elegant room with lots of red drapes and nicely panelled wood etc. There are a few ransoms sat there drinking. As soon as we walk in, big T has a word with this older but attractive woman and then the ransoms are asked to drink up and basically fuck off. They glance at us with a look of disapproval, but fuck them. Immediately the doors are locked behind them and shutters, and I mean proper metal shutters, are pulled down. I'm not concerned as Big T has obviously arranged something. But I am intrigued as to what is coming up. Well, basically thirteen Asian whores proceed to walk out and even themselves out between the five of us. I nabbed three being the greedy fucker I am. For next two hours I was blown, had my arse licked out while I was fingering and kissing any available hole in these three slut whores who were each taking turns to suck my balls, cock and lick the choco freeway clean...carnage all with my trousers still around my ankles. It's a bizarre sight seeing slags all blowing your pals while drinks are being served and also, periodically, big T walking around laughing like a stupid cunt and tipping beer on all of our cocks so the slags could suck it off...fucking heaven. Think about it, how many times have we all spent fortunes trying to shag some good-looking bitch by taking her to dinner etc. Fuck it, get locked into this place and take the thinking out of the process. So back to it. I had shot the population paint a couple of times in these bitches' mouths and stopped for a smoke and beer while they toyed with the purple warrior getting him ready for action again. I'm slouched back like a fucking lord. Great!!! So back to the sucking routine again and after a while I grab the best-looking one out of the three and get her to roll on the rubber lifesaver and ride me on top. I make the other two kiss over me while I have a finger up each of their wet cunts...awesome coordination...so I am getting a good fucking off this Asian slut. Then I decide to sit up straight moving the kissing pair out of the way. I fling my arms around her waist and now pick up this bird I am fucking and penguin walk like a stupid cunt with my trousers round my ankles up to the bar and fuck her as hard as possible against it. The lads are cheering and I'm pleased to say she shot her load way before I did. It must have been the severe top knocking off all three of them had just done but she looked fucking exhausted after her pummelling had finished. She was a cute tiny little slut and I'm sure she felt it afterwards...but fuck, it call it a work hazard.

Meanwhile the lads are now doing a domino effect of shooting their loads into these whores all around the room...fucking hilarious. Everyone cleans up with the standard supply of moist wipes these sluts carry to clean your bell end before they start to blow the pipe of life dry. With lots of laughing and a couple more beers we all piss off out not before passing £200 a piece to the attractive older bird who is obviously the madam-in-charge...most likely ex-brass herself as they usually are. That must be like promotion in the whore world. Hilarious. We trot off to find a bar and reflect on what just happened. Big T is looking all pleased with himself, smug twat, but love the tosser. We all part company and big T asks if I need dropping back. I decline and say my goodbyes. That's not the end though, me being me. Bearing in mind I am pretty smashed by now I decide to check into a hotel in the West End and order in some more pussy to my room. I was rampant as the more I thought about our nice 'lock-in' the hornier I got. So, after a few calls and negotiations, this cute Swedish whore knocks on my room door. I let her in and proceed to fuck the arse off her. She ended up staying the whole night which allowed me to convince her to let me nudge the old boy into her shit pipe and bolt up there as well. Nice finish to the night of carnage.

I love fingering birds while arse-fucking them. It's so weird feeling your own cock through the skin bridge between her pussy andarsehole... awesome. I woke up about 11am to her showering. She kissed me goodbye and I got up, paid the bill and went and found a greasy spoon. I phoned big T to tell him. He laughed like fuck...another night out with the boys!!

3 Hired help

This particular night, in January 2005 I think, it

was typically pissing down with rain and fucking freezing; my nuts were like shrivelled raisins. The band had been booked to play at a private function in a posh marquee for a load of rich twats. Big dollars for an hour's set...very nice. The backline guys had all the gear set up when we got there and after a few glasses of wine we decide to do a sound check. How very nice of us. Couple of whacks on my kit and by now I am fully awake and already scouring the venue for pussy. There are a lot of horny catering girls, Polish of course, and event organiser-type chicks that seem to do fuck all but carry clipboards and revel in the fact they have walkie-talkies or fucking earpieces in so they can liaise and ensure that the flowers need freshening or some bullshit like that. Once our sound check is over, it's the worst fucking time as we have around three hours to kill before we even have to think about playing. Mmm, watch a film on the laptop or go for the drink and possible chick-fucking option. Sorry, Bruce, but Enter the Dragon can wait for another day.

Our clipboard chick that's been allocated to look after us is about twenty-three to twenty-fiveish, dark hair, olive skin. Clarissa, hot as fuck, bit stuck-up, but I got the impression it was only how she thought she was supposed to be for the job. I asked her to get some vodka for me and, on her return, insisted she join me in one. Very reluctantly she agreed, being worried that she might be caught drinking on the job, with the fucking drummer…hilarious. I started my usual cheeky naughty banter to make her laugh, not caring what I said out loud. Interestingly this tactic works very well on slightly reserved girls as you end up saying things out loud they are only possibly thinking. Having this in someone else makes them warm to you in that 'he's a bit of a naughty boy' way. As we chatted and laughed I noticed her getting more open and touchy-feely, responding to my gutter humour. The radar was up (so was my cock), she had to go off a few times to sort something out and I stayed on my spot, vodka in hand. I could see the rest of the band looking over and smiling with 'that dirty cunt is at it again' look. She eventually came back apologising for taking too long (good sign). Now I smoke like hell and was dying for a cigarette so I asked if she would come outside for one with me. She followed accordingly. Once outside she said, "There's a quiet store near the kitchen access for the catering that may be a warmer place to smoke." Now I kid you not, once inside she fucking changed into a demon, throwing down my cigarette and grabbing at my cock through my jeans. After kissing her hard I put my hands on her shoulders and pushed her down on her knees. She didn't resist and quickly took out my throbbing rod and noshed the fuck out of it...fucking bliss. I'm grabbing her ponytail and helping her back and forth (go do your bit). Now this is something you don't often get from a girl: after shooting my baby gravy down her neck (she took the lot down, no problem) she then started to gently lick and suck my balls while I recovered from the shoot and then put my cum-dripping semi into her mouth until I got hard as fuck again. Now I took charge! I bent her over one of the flight cases in the store, hitched up her little work skirt, pulled her tiny panties to one side and rammed my cock into her dripping cunt, pummelled the arse off this girl and at one point had to put my hand over her mouth to shut up her loud moaning. Fuck getting caught, I wanted to keep fucking her. The funny thing was her radio was periodically going off asking her location. I was tempted to answer for her but resisted. I came again inside her (not proud but I barebacked her like a horny mindless idiot). After we had both rearranged our clothes we left the store separately and went back in. Well, not before I stopped for a smoke and pondered what had just happened...fucking awesome. The best bit was nobody including the lads had a clue...until I told them later, that is, what had happened. She carried on being professional for the rest of the night. One thing that impressed me was that somehow she had managed to slip her business card into my pocket to give me her mobile number. I found out later she had done this as she was grabbing at my knob in the store and had planned it on the way out. That's impressive work.

After the gig finished, I texted her on the way back home north of the river and thirty minutes later she replied, 'Send me your address, I am getting into a cab and I want fucking hard in your bed tonight'...fucking awesome. She arrived, walked in my apartment, didn't say a word, just stripped down to her undies and let me lead the way into the bedroom. I obliged with the lack of talk, ripped off the undies and fucked her from all angles. She liked it hard and a bit rough in a good way...just some pinning her down stuff and talking filth to her while banging the juice out of her wet pastie!! Fuck knows what time we got to sleep but we were both knackered and sweating like fuck. We woke up, kissed and played for a bit then had a nice spoon fuck. We went out for brekkie (greasy spoon, I know how to treat a girl) then I sent her on her way. We hooked up a few times again when we could but I stopped calling her. You can't do them for too long or they start to want to pick curtains in IKEA...fuck that shit.

4 Double bubble

My ex-bird had some fit mates. You already know where this is heading! One of them, Sarah, used to be married and came to stay at our place once when things were getting rough towards the end of her relationship with her now ex-hubby...he was a nice bloke but a fucking disaster of life who couldn't quite make anything work. Sarah was blonde, big tits, great arse and very pretty, a little bimboesque but nice with it. She always dressed nicely and never left home without make-up, that sort of girl. A good laugh as well which I always like and makes life much easier when you're trying to get into the knickers. Before I go on let me tell you about my ex: she was very adventurous in the sack and we often role-played about a threesome with someone we both knew and fancied. She was a fucking nightmare to be with as her bloke but that's a different story. So Sarah comes over and we all have dinner and laughs and loads of wine and vodka, etc, etc. The girls as usual got very giggly It was a hot summer evening, all the windows open in the apartment and they decided, the more pissed they got, that it would be fun to shower together to cool off...radar cock time. I played it cool and let them go off to the bathroom, smoked a couple of cigarettes and had another vodka before heading towards the giggling noise from the bathroom. I casually walked in to find both girls with fuck all on in the shower together just laughing and actually showering...what a fucking horny sight that was. Neither of them cared that I was there and my bird said, "Come in and join us." It would have been far too crowded in the shower cubicle so I opened the sliding doors and dropped my trousers and showed them both my massive hard-on. My bird grabbed it and started to wank me off. Sarah just watched while soaping herself then eventually touching her cunt...lovely. My bird gets down and starts to blow me big time and I can see Sarah is into this in a huge way. I usher her to get down and join in. My bird very kindly obliges and lets her suck me off while she kisses my balls all over...it was fucking amazing. Sarah made me come big time in her mouth and then immediately started to snog the face of my girl with a mouthful of my cum. This was fucking unreal…every man's dream. I announced I was going to get some drinks and would see them both in the bedroom. By the time I returned they were both lying on my bed licking each other's cunts, still soaking wet from the shower. Fuck, I was rock hard again by now and decided to carry on my attentions to Sarah as, who knows, this might never happen again. I pulled my bird's face away from her pussy and slid my cock into her cunt as deep and as fast as possible. She moaned like fuck as I rammed her hard with my empty but soon to be refilled nuts slamming against her sexy tight arse. By now my bird had positioned herself in front of her and had forced Sarah's head onto her tight little cunt again for a good licking.

She watched me as I fucked her friend from behind and had this real look of almost sadistic pleasure on her face, only occasionally looking down to watch her friend give her lingus. I fucked both of them from all angles for hours and my bird encouraged Sarah to let me do her in the arse as she knew she hadn't ever tried it. Who am I to argue?! Not only did she get her arse broken in that night, the devil in me also shot my load up there to really initiate her into the back door club...love my own work. We all fell asleep in a heap of sweat and cum juice. I woke first and cooked some breakfast to wake up my two dirty little sluts. Everything was cool with the girls and we all chatted openly about the evening's fun and games. The girls got ready and buggered off for a day up West shopping their tits off. That's means one thing in my book: call in a fuckin' whore ASAP. Straight on the blower to book the fittest slut money could buy. An hour and a half later this Brazilian bird rocks up to the apartment. Legs like they wouldn't end and the prettiest of faces, great pert tits, a real head turner. A glass of wine later we were on the bed. She was slow and sensual and in no rush. She slowly unzipped me, teased and licked my cock until it was weeping like a baby with anticipation. She then stood up and slowly undressed down to her sexy black underwear and only then continued to suck me off making very sexual eye contact (not with my japs) as she gave one of the most beautiful blows I have ever had...warm, no fucking teeth scraping (which I hate) just fucking awesome. She cupped my nuts gently and built it up until I was ready to shoot. She knew her job very fucking well and she deep throated me as I fucking exploded like a white emulsion warhead...unbelievable. I decided that was all I needed, paid her and off she went on her merry little whore way. Now I kid you not, it must have been some weird voodoo intuition shit as about twenty-five minutes later the girls rocked in much earlier than I ever thought muttering they couldn't be arsed shopping so had had lunch, a few wines and come home. I'm thinking, good job I didn't fuck that brass as it could have got very interesting had they walked in on my bare arse in the air pumping away on the Brazilian beauty...close shave. By the way, Sarah and I met independently after the threesome for some more sex...mainly up the arse was the focus of our crafty get-togethers!! She is now re-married...not the first time I have been to a wedding that I have fucked the bride shortly before.

5 Sharon the dancer

A good pal of mine is an entertainer from Australia. He called me to say he would be in London staying for ten days near Richmond as his dancers were rehearsing in town before they joined a cruise ship for a six-month contract. They had accommodation in a really nice river-facing apartment and he suggested I come over and stay so we could catch up and have a few drinks and laughs. He is like an Aussie version of me so we get along just great.

I turn up at this place and he is by himself but there is girls' stuff everywhere. He tells me his bird is with him and a dancer called Sharon but they are in rehearsals all day and won't be back until later. He tells me Sharon has just been fucked around by this twat she fell for in Oz who has basically dumped her by e-mail and confessed to shagging around while she was gone. She is very down and upset so it could be tricky to fuck her. His advice is to keep it cool and see what transpires; all taken on board. After a day of shooting the shit with him and drinking on the balcony, the girls turn up in their dance gear knackered. My mate's bird is very sweet and makes the effort to chat but Sharon who is a twenty-three-year-old old hottie BTW, is not so open and obviously pre-occupied as I was warned. The girls go off to shower and change and we all go down to the local boozer for food and drinks. We had fun and listened to some God-awful rock covers band (drummer was pretty good though...he recognised me which was a pain and came over to talk shop for a bit during their break). This helped a bit though with the chat to Sharon as she didn't know what I did. However she wasn't showing any signs of coming over to the dark side. I paid for dinner under protest from them all but I am big on making people welcome to our town if possible. We all walked back slightly pissed and had more drinks back at the apartment. The girls bailed early as they had an early start to get to rehearsals and left me and my pal to carry on boozing. I asked him about Sharon. He said, "Who knows, she's fucked up over this idiot in Oz so I'll sound her out when

I get the chance."

The next day I had to go off to do some recording work and made arrangements to see them at the weekend. I had been invited to go to Twickenham on the Sunday for a game which worked out great as it was a booze-filled day and afterwards I got dropped off at the same boozer that we had had dinner in the other night. My pal and the girls were holed up in the corner drinking and I rocked in half-pissed and full of banter, larger than life. It was perfect as I came straight in and ordered loads of shots and got them on it big time playing spoof for shots of Jagermeister and aftershock. Sharon was in a much better mood and I made lots of fuss of her, making her laugh and not letting her buy drinks, etc...just being a smooth twat basically. My pal said, "She likes you, mate. She told my girl, so keep on her and play the fun guy so she stops moping over this Oz prick." This was all discussed while pissing in the gents. Loads more booze later we headed back. Sharon was hanging onto me all the way back and kept saying it was lovely to meet me and thanks for a fun night. (I'm thinking it ain't over yet, girl.) My mate's girl crashed as soon as we got back; she was smashed. The rest of us drank, smoked and chatted outside on the balcony for ages. By the way, my pal is a cunt; he was hanging on in the hope of fucking her too, the randy tosspot. Sharon announced she was feeling a bit sick and went off to the toilet. This was my opportunity. I fucked him off to bed, got a glass of water and went to the toilet to check on Sharon. She had been a bit sick and was grateful for the water. She cleaned her teeth and I carried the water to her room for her. She took off her jeans and lay sideways on her bed. I gave her some more water and rubbed her back before gradually lying down beside her. She snuggled her arse into my cock which of course was ready for action by now. Well, fuck me, this fit little dancer in her tiny French knickers pushing into me, what can you do?! I started to kiss her neck and gently played with and fingered her pussy, then headed down to kiss her stomach and eventually pulled her knickers to one side to lick out her pussy. She was into it big time. I pulled off her knickers and took off her top and bra so she was there naked on the bed. As quick as a flash I stripped off as well. I carried on licking her and every minute or so would come up and stick my tongue down her throat covered in her pussy juice. She loved it. I started to rub my hard cock over her pussy slapping it on her clit and rubbing it up and down her wet cunt lips just slipping it in slightly to tease her, turning into a screaming for me to fuck her animal. I fucked her big time, long and hard. She was cock possessed and came on me like a fucking waterfall. Having copious amounts of booze inside me I hadn't shot yet so turned her around and fucked her hard from behind. She was a tiny little thing but liked cock rammed into her hard. She was shouting at me to fuck her hard so of course I obliged and gave her tight little arse a few slaps along the way which helped her come again. I ended up with her sucking me off while I straddled her face and coming all over it and into her mouth which she was into. All this in a single bed. We both crashed and I woke before her. Being the shit that I am, I lifted the covers and took some phone film of her in bed before going through to the lounge. My pal was already up and smiled like a bastard when I came through. I made him smell my fingers being the twat that I am and we watched the phone film together with him calling me a cunt every few seconds. We were sat on the balcony smoking when the girls appeared showered and ready to leave. Both girls pecked us on the cheeks and left for rehearsals again. We spent the day laughing about my conquest before me saying my goodbyes. We still laugh about that today when we talk.

6 Sherry

I met Sherry who is the wife of a guy I know only through the music industry. He is a complete tosser but one of those people you have to put up with for work, etc. I fucking hate that shit but sometimes we all have to endure that bollocks in life. Sherry is mid-thirties, a real horny MILF, two young kids with a dick of a husband who gives her a nice lifestyle and the price she pays is being stuck with his cunt-like ways. So here we are (the band) at some swanky event at the Dorchester all on this table suited and booted (more shit I hate), ten of us all eating, drinking, etc. I'm sitting next to Sherry who has always flirted with me. Being the cheeky wanker that I am, I always promoted it heavily even in front of the twat hubby just to knob him off. Just banter even though I always wanted to fuck the arse off her. The night progressed and we got more and more pissed.

Sherry in particular started to suffer after I insisted she do vodka shots with me. Hubby had ignored her all night and, in her drunken state, she started to confide in me that he is a wanker, never pays her attention and, on the rare occasions that he sleeps with her, is crap in bed!! Now you don't have to say things like that twice to a pussy predator like me. I brushed her leg with my finger and told her he must be fucking blind and stupid as if she was with me I would treat her like a queen and fuck her stupid at every opportunity. She blushed up but said, "That sounds like heaven." My response: "Let's make it happen now!" She said she wanted to big time but was scared of being seen, caught, etc, etc, all that I'm married shit. I suggested she slip away to the ladies and I would meet her outside in ten minutes and while she was out there to hatch a plan to get fucking me as soon as possible (upfront as hell but she was loving it). I watched her hubby as she left and he didn't even notice her go, he was deep in bullshit city with some corporate boring tosser. My watch couldn't have moved slower and I was horny as fuck with the anticipation of sexing this bored MILF. Right on cue I am outside the ladies and she appears seconds later, make-up refreshed and a look of excitement on her cute face. She walks up to me and whispers, "Follow me." I'm impressed. I walk a couple of steps behind just for discretion. She walks to the hotel lift, in we get. She announces once inside, waving a room card, that we are going up to the room that her and husband are staying in that night... awesome. We kissed and groped a bit in the lift, but cooled it off before it stopped in case of bumping into anyone either of us knew. Coast clear we rushed to the room, got in as quickly as possible and within seconds I had her dress lifted up, panties to one side and gave her pussy a massive licking and clit-sucking experience. She was forcing her cunt onto my tongue and was shouting out loud with pleasure. Hubby obviously doesn't know his way to the little man in the boat. She came all over my face and turned around against the wall and told me to fuck her from behind. One hard cock out later I obliged. She was screaming for me to fuck her hard and had both hands against the wall clawing at the wallpaper as I did just that to her. This was horny as fuck. I was soon ready to shoot my porridge and told her; she pulled out my cock, turned around, dropped to her knees, rammed my cock into her mouth and gulped down my cum like a Mac D's thick shake. It was intense. The whole lick fuck and come session must have only spanned fifteen minutes max. We were both so intensely turned on it didn't matter it was a short session. I kissed her as passionately as I could muster after her just taking down my jizz. Being a typical bloke it's very OK for her to swallow but the kissing thing after isn't the greatest...but you have to show willing at times. We cleaned up and got back down to the dinner as soon as we could. Under my lead we walked in together as bold as brass. Me, being the sly fucker that I am, carried in my cigarettes and lighter and made a very obvious placement of them on the table as we both sat down so it looked like I had returned from a cigarette. I immediately struck up idle banter with her at the table. Nobody even noticed or suspected foul play...the perfect shag crime!!

I fucked Sherry often after that at hotels, in my car, her car and, best of all, in her marital bed twice while tosser hubby was away on business. I felt a bit bad about that as I snuck into the house late on both occasions while their two young kids were asleep and fucked the arse off Mummy and snuck back out again in the early hours. Bit bad because of the kids but no harm done there. I had to cool her off slowly though in the end as she started to show signs of wanting to leave hubby for me and even mentioned the L word at one point...hold your fucking horses, love…cock you can have...a fucking store card and dinner on the table ain't happening. She still texts me on the odd occasion. Still unhappy and still has this thing for me; well, the carefree fucking and excitement that I can so easily bring while I have no strings attached my end, more like. I have seen her husband a number of times as well and always laugh inside like fuck that I have fucked his wife from all angles and he has no clue. He did say to me once, "My missus has a soft spot for you," but I just laughed it off and no more was said... clueless fucking mug.

7 Just Jo

Jo was a sexy, strawberry haired, slim twenty-four-year-old that I used to see on occasions when it suited us both. Basically the whole relationship consisted of drinks and usually risky intense sex.

Jo worked in finance in the City and was a typical party city girl who hailed from Essex but worked in town. I met her at a friend's BBQ in Guildford of all places. We were immediately attracted to each other and hit it off. Both single, lots of banter and loved a party. The day we met we spent a good hour taking the piss out of each other, then lined up tequila shots both pretty smashed and flirting like hell. I whispered in her ear that I wanted to fuck her right now, and near enough dragged her off to the nearest toilet in my pal's place and skinhead fucked her against the sink (basically what I call a skinhead fuck is ripping the panties off and shoving your cock inside her and proceed to fuck as hard and as quick as possible...preferably both coming together. Zip up and just leave her there with Harry Monk running down her legs). Jo loved it and came back to the garden minutes later and just carried on drinking with me...my kind of girl.

One momentous occasion with Jo consisted of me supposedly picking her up from her office after work for drinks and whatever the night brought along. I met her in the reception area and thought we were going straight out. Jo had other plans!

She took me to the lift giving me some bullshit about a quick tour of the office. As soon as we got in the lift she was all over me unzipping my cock and wanking me waiting only until bell goes for our floor giving me seconds to put my rigid old man away, the bitch. Payback, I suppose. She shows me around the office. There are still a few randoms working who pay no attention to us both. Good job as I had this very noticeable semi showing. Jo had the devil in her eyes as she led me through to her office. No sooner had we got inside than she had undone her blouse and dropped her skirt down revealing her skimpy underwear and sat up on her desk stroking her pussy through her panties. Horny as fuck, down came my trousers and out with the rod of plenty and immediately went in deep on her over her desk pumping away at her wet cunt like an animal. I popped her tits out of her bra and sucked hard on her gorgeous little nipples as I fucked her. Five minutes later max, I am shooting my man fat up inside her as she is coming like a tap all over my cock...intense fucking at its finest. Jo just smiled at me as she went down on her knees and kissed all over my tingling cum-dripping cock before angling the semi-blood back into my trousers. Fucking dirty little bitch, she was awesome. I know the office was pretty empty but any fucker could have walked in on us, but she didn't care...nice work.

We left shortly after that and went out on the smash in the West End getting pissed as arseholes, totally oblivious of anyone around us. That kind of summed this thing with Jo: she was intense when she wanted to be and didn't care about who or what was around us. It was very refreshing to find a bird like this. She wasn't a keeper but great fun to be with and fucked like a caveman. Later on we stumbled out of some bar and ended up fucking again in a doorway just off Piccadilly. Again no world records, just intense risky sex just how she liked it. She took my cum in her mouth this time and swallowed it down like honey off a spoon and then, laughing like a mad woman, she was funny as fuck, a bit unhinged, I reckon. We hailed a black cab and fell into my place pissed, straight onto the bed, both of us must have passed out in seconds. I woke up early dying for a slash fully clothed with Jo next to me fully clothed as well, fucking hilarious. I pissed, showered and got in beside her and undressed her without her stirring and gave her a wake-up call by licking all over her clit. She soon woke and had hold of my hair pushing me into her clit. As she was getting close to coming, I got up and pushed my cock into her so she could come on me. After she had come I took out my cock and wanked all over her lovely tits, then sent her off to the shower. I did have breakfast waiting for her so I'm not all bad! She got ready and went on her merry way, happy as fuck.

I kind of lost touch with Jo, no real reason, it just was what it was and we both enjoyed the fun. I remember once she was sucking me off big time while I was driving the car on the M25 and I actually paid my pound into the auto-toll at the Dartford tunnel while she carried on...I think I might give her a call – see what she's up to!!

The Footballer

There is no way of saying this except to say that this guy takes the very definition of being wrong to new dimensions. He has done everything; even when he should be on his best behaviour playing for his country, he has two girls lined up to meet him once he has finished. Like a lot of football players he is a big old unit and 6'3", so quite a presence, but because he plays in defence his body is a lot bigger. He is a good-looking guy, loves the champagne lifestyle and really loves chasing women. I first met him at a private party. There were only two women left at the end of the night and maybe six guys all trying their luck. Well, he kissed both and told me he'd just chosen the one with the biggest tits and left the other girls like loose change.

He's a marvel, über-professional when playing, doesn't drink, eats so well and trains like a maniac. His mantra is you've got to earn your piss, translated if you over-indulge and wake up feeling like crap from the night before, just get on with the day, and for him that's training until you feel sick. He has so much confidence and silent charm, I kid you not, he can get whatever woman he wants and, being a footballer helps, plus he has the chat. Over the years he has won the premiership in England, been capped twice and can run the hundred in 10.8. But that is nothing compared to how fast he can pick up women! Mr S is every mum's worst nightmare as you just don't see him coming.

My opinion of women has changed slightly over the past year or two, but I suppose I would have to call myself a chauvinist. Women obviously have a different more sensitive approach to everything and because I am able to manipulate them, because of this sensitive nature, I think they are weak. That sounds worse than it is. I am a great believer that a man and a woman who have never met before will not be friends unless there is some attraction from one or both parties. This excludes old friends, people you grew up with or have known through somebody else for a long time, although it is still often the case. When it comes to pulling, for me it is about confidence. This comes easily to me because I do think that I can pull most girls I see. This is why I am often accused of being arrogant, but it is just confidence in my own ability and as I always get the girl I want why should I doubt myself? If you don't back yourself no one else will!! Normally when I walk in to a place, straightaway I am scanning the room for potential targets. If I see something I like I will try and make eye contact and then go from there. I love the game; that's why I can never be faithful, the thrill of the chase I suppose, even if I know the eventual outcome. Women who know me, or know of me, will mostly bad-mouth me, call me a player or whatever, but at the end of the day, if they had a chance they would. FACT. Proven that many times even with ex-girlfriends' best mates who slate me to them for ages and then I end up banging them: girls who don't know me at all, that varies from people thinking I'm arrogant, to girls just coming over to me to tell me they think I'm hot. That's obviously the best scenario, but can get annoying as over fifty per cent of the confident women who come up to me are below average.

1 Not your average night out

When I was living with Steve, a few of us had a couple of days off from training so we decided to go out. Rachel, who I was seeing at the time, had gone back to the Devon with her brother. She called me and asked if I would get her brother's girlfriend into Elysium that night. I think it was a Saturday night. I didn't really like the girl but I said fine, no problems. I told Rachel to give Linda, Ben's girlfriend, my number, which she did. Anyway, Linda called me. I was with all the footballer boys on Steve's roof terrace. We were having a few drinks and were about to go out. We had a few pills too just to get us in the mood and Linda rang me. She asked if she and a friend could come out with us rather than going out on their own. I wasn't sure but as she was almost family, and I thought it would get me some brownie points with the missus, and the boys were keen, I gave her Steve's address and she headed over in a taxi. By the time she arrived with her friend we were all pretty loose, and we went on the piss around Fulham. As soon as she arrived, she basically started saying to me, "I know you want to fuck me. I know you want to fuck me. I can tell by the way you look at me." Initially I told her to fuck off, but she kept on at me saying, "I've seen how you look at my tits, they're better than Rachel's, do you want to see them?" Anyway, I ended up getting fucking pissed and the idea of fucking her didn't seem so ridiculous; she was really tidy too. I disappeared to get some coke from my mate down the road and, on the way back, one of the lads I was out with called me and said, "You need to get back here and see what this bird's doing." So I walked into this boozer and two of the boys were fingering her at the bar, she was absolutely loving it and, as you can imagine, the boys were too. We went next door and she was getting on my case again. I'd had a few lines by this point and she was giving it all the "you know you want to fuck me, you know you want to fuck me" again so I thought, fuck this, and took her into the disabled toilets, laid her down and did her over the sink while I was looking at her in the mirror giving it the American psycho pose. She loved it, couldn't get enough, and was telling me to do her harder. She turned as I came and swallowed the lot as if insatiable.

As soon as I got out of the toilet leaving her still in there cleaning herself up, I went to the bar, got my mate and said, "Right, we're going." I just wanted to get out of there. My mate knew straightaway what I had done and why I wanted to leave so he said nothing and followed me out. We ended up going to Blue, a club round the corner. We were regulars so the door staff let us in ahead of the queue. We said hi to the owner's daughter and headed straight for VIP. Once we got seated we got straight back on it and invited a few girls to join us. I got talking to a girl called Jane. She was all over me and obviously keen as mustard, so after a couple of shots and a cheeky line in the DJ booth with the promoter we left. She only lived round the corner in Chelsea. Now this girl was the kind that wanted to be told what to do; you can tell these girls a mile off. This was ideal as I didn't want to hang around, so as soon as we set foot in the flat I dropped my pants and gave her instructions. As my heart wasn't in it and I really wanted to be back on the smash with the boys, I gave her one and then went straight back to Blue. I got back in just as it was closing and met Steve and the other lads who were all fucked. On the way back to my mate's house, I came across this blonde Scandinavian bird and started having a bit of banter with her on the street. She was gorgeous, straight out of a Swedish porn vid, she REALLY was worth shagging even with the previous exploits. So I invited her back to Steve's house for a 'party', and me and another mate ended up having a threesome with her as others were filming. The thing I'll never forget is that while we were fucking her, my mate's girlfriend was fingering herself watching these two big football guys go through this innocent student at 4am. Fucking priceless.

This one night I was out with a girl I met through my best mate's brother. I had first met her at my mate's brother's boarding school, one of the best and most expensive in the country. She was absolutely loaded, serious old school money, and had the most amazing accent, so posh it was cool. Her dad had owned a huge advertising company, but had sold up and was a known tax exile. The thing about this girl was that, inconsistent with her privileged background, for all the privileges she'd had she was Lady Muck and she loved to party. I mean she got right on it. I first met this bird when I was playing down south. I ended up getting hold of her years back but hadn't spoken to her for ages. Anyway when Facebook first came out I saw her name come up on a friend's home page, so I got in touch but I was still with my bird at the time so had to be a little covert! After she had accepted my friend's request, we messaged back and forth and arranged to meet up for dinner. I hadn't seen her for years so didn't really know what to expect. All I knew was that she looked hot in her pictures on Facebook, and that last time I saw her we got right on it and had great sex. We arranged to meet in a bar in Soho, then went on to a restaurant around the corner. We were hammering the double vodkas and getting on like a house on fire. She's only a small girl, really, really petite but with a big set of tits on her, a dirty bitch with a playboy tattoo on her lower back. We were both starting to get pissed and relax a little more. I started to want a line but didn't want to suggest anything in case it wasn't her thing. No sooner had this gone through my mind than she asked me if I wanted any, fucking excellent. I made a phone call and had a couple of grams dropped off. We started smashing it, then went for our dinner reservation and moved on to the Dom Perignon. We left the restaurant an hour later after eating none of our food and spending most of our time in the toilets sniffing, and we went to a club.

We went straight in, said a few pleasantries to the door staff that always looked after me, went downstairs and straight into the disabled toilets for a quick sniff. She followed me in. Before I knew it we were all over each other. I turned her round, hitched up her skirt, ripped off her knickers and started hammering her. We were in there for a good twenty minutes fucking and snorting coke. She was putting coke on my cock whilst sucking it off. It was fantastic. When we eventually left the cubicle we were both pretty dishevelled and decided to go back to her flat as she was absolutely arseholed. We left in a taxi, I called my man and got some more gear in. It was only half one. After making a pickup en route we arrived at her flat. She is an absolute mess and can hardly stand. She had mentioned earlier in the night that she was sharing a house with her sister who is only nineteen whom I'd never met but I'd heard stories about her: a model and apparently an absolute caner too just like her sis, into all sorts of stuff, meth, hard drugs, partying, pills, but absolutely gorgeous tight body, big tits, dark hair, fucking beautiful. She opened the door and the stories were true.

Anyway we go through to the kitchen and make some drinks. I put out a couple of lines, but my date tells me she is going to bed. She was that fucked I wasn't going to disagree. So I'm sitting there racking up a couple of lines and twisted thinking, fuck, I want to get on it and she's gone to bed. Thinking of my options I politely ask her sister who is still downstairs with me if she would like one. She says, "Oh, I shouldn't" with a glint in her eyes and a cheeky smile. She told me she had university in the morning and if she had a line she wouldn't sleep. It's pretty obvious she wants one, so after a little gentle persuasion, she tucks in. We get right on it, put some music on, got the champagne out and polished off the rest of the coke. So her sister's upstairs and we start chatting and it turns to relationships. I drop in how beautiful she is and how it is a crime that she is single. She was loving it and knew exactly what I was getting at. She brought up the issue of her sister which I rubbished saying that I hadn't met her and that it was just a bit of fun. Eventually she comes over and grabs me; ha, brilliant, so we start kissing. I take her up to her room next to her sister's and start kissing her and stripping her, and end up having the filthiest sex, all the while her elder sister, my date, is passed out next door. Anyways, the next morning, I'll never forget. I've passed out naked in bed and her sister has woken up massively hungover, can hardly remember the night before let alone me fucking her in the toilets. She walks in, sees me naked in bed with her sister, condom wrappers on the floor and goes absolutely apeshit, it was hilarious. I had to bite the inside of my cheeks to stop myself from laughing. I quickly got dressed and made a sharp exit before things turned really ugly. The funniest thing after all was that I still ended up fucking the older sister two months later!

3 Strippers and coffee shops

When I'm playing midweek, I can't go out, or do much at all as I'm training the next day so I can't really go boozing. So me and a couple of the lads got into the habit of going to strip clubs on a Tuesday and Wednesday night, you know, to get us out of the house! Just having a bit of a perv but not drinking. So we'd go in on Tuesday and Wednesday night and, as most doormen recognise us, they'd let us in for free, and let us know if the B team were working that night. We'd go in, have a look around, have a couple of dances and chat to the birds. Strippers on the whole are obviously easy, I mean they take their clothes off for a living, and the fact that they do this means that most of them are in really good shape. What a combination: good-looking girls who are easy! Definitely the best entertainment a young man can get on a school night. We would have a bit of banter with the girls and if any of them looked half decent we'd get their numbers and, more often than not, end up shagging them the same night as they'd call you after they'd finished. As I said, easy.

Anyway, there was this one time I met this half-caste girl in one of my local haunts called Liana, absolutely amazing looking, big tits, dark hair, looked like Pocahontas with a great tan, and I used to nail her all the time. We had unbelievable sex. She was amazing; all she wanted was to be fucked up the arse, so much she'd cry for it, in fact she could only come that way, and shout, "Fuck me in the arse, you prick!" She also knew exactly where she stood. The night I had asked for her number she had said, "So you just want sex, yeah?" Initially I thought it was a trick question but thought, fuck it and said yeah. It turned out that was all she wanted so we had a perfect little arrangement. Anyway, after knowing her for a month or two, I was out on the smash with the footy boys and called her up about 4am. I told her I was going to get dropped off at her house which she said was fine so I gave the taxi driver her address. The thing I hadn't told her was that I was with one of my mates. So we arrive at her house and I ring the doorbell already planning an excuse for my friend's presence. When she opened the door she just looked at me, looked at my mate, and said, "Come in." I was slightly confused but thought fair play. I went straight in, didn't say anything, walked into her room and dropped my kecks thinking, let's see how easy you are. She started sucking me off. So she's sucking with my mate watching who has a huge grin on his face. So I say to her, "Don't be rude, look after my friend too." He looked a little uneasy but without batting an eyelid she turns to my mate and starts wanking him off. I told her to get naked, she obliged and I start fucking her doggy style whilst she is sucking off my mate. She tells me to stop, disappears into her cupboard and returns with a vibrating cock ring and asks me to put it on. We both end up spit-roasting her. Shagging her in her every hole, really disgraceful behaviour, but she is loving it.

Anyway this became a regular occurrence over the next few weeks. I must have taken six or seven mates around, always doing the same thing. She loved it and never ever said no!

There was this one time I was having trouble with

my missus. We were arguing and stuff, so I'd wait until she fell asleep then sneak out without waking her and head out. This one time I went out and went to see the stripper about 3am, popped into hers, fucked the arse off her for an hour then headed home. As I was training so much all the extra energy spent meant I was always hungry. So on the way home I stopped at the local Esso garage to grab some food. Anyways I'm waiting to pay and there is this bird behind me. She keeps looking at me; she is Polish or Eastern European or something. Tall and skinny with a beautiful face, she keeps looking so I start having a bit of banter with her in the queue and it turns out she is going the same way as me so I start talking and suggest we head back together. Anyway I start giving her the chat and when I get near Wandsworth Bridge Road where I live she tells me that she has a boyfriend but really likes me etc. She suggests that we go somewhere for a late drink. All I was interested in was shagging her, but there were a few problems. We couldn't go to my flat which was just down the road as my girlfriend was asleep in bed and as she lived locally I didn't want her to know where I lived. We can't go to her house as her boyfriend is there, and I can't be bothered to get a hotel. So as we approach my front door I am resigned to the fact that the evening's festivities are at an end. Except just down the road I see a Starbucks near where I live and, as I walk past, I notice that the front door is ajar. Unbelievable, I couldn't believe my luck. I said, "Come on, let's go in." She says, "No, no, what if someone comes in?" I said, "Fuck it, we'll just say we were trying to find someone to tell them that the door wasn't locked, and we're not going to rob anything, are we." So we went into the back of the kitchen and start kissing. She started to worry about getting caught, but once I alleviated her concerns and we had got started she wasn't complaining. We had the craziest sex all over the kitchen, both giggling at how naughty we were being; she even rode me on one of the couches in the café where I had sat many times having a grande latte and a piece of rocky road! Anyways we've finished and, after getting dressed, I go to leave, but my front door is clearly visible from the café, and now I really don't want her to know where I live so I throw her a dummy. After saying goodbye and reassuring her that we would go for dinner the following night, I left, walked in the opposite direction to my flat and hid quietly around the corner waiting for her to disappear out of sight. As soon as she had gone I ran back to my front door and quickly let myself in. After a very quiet shower, I went upstairs and got into bed with my girlfriend who was sound asleep, and none the wiser that I had just fucked two girls while she had been asleep.

4 She bit off more than she could chew

Me and a few of the boys went out on the lash. We went to a club in the West End and had a table in the VIP room. As it was the weekend and we didn't have a game, we could go hard. We went downstairs into the VIP area and got seated by our hostess and put in a huge order of champagne belvedere, the works, you name it, and it was on the table. There were four or five girls sat around a table facing us, all top of the range and all looking over at our table as we were being pretty boisterous as usual. One of these girls was an absolute dead ringer for Paris Hilton who I'm a big fan of, and she couldn't take her eyes off me. So after a few looseners and a quick scan around to make sure that there was nothing better kicking about, I sent a bottle of champagne over to break the ice. The girls are made up with the champagne, and they come over to our table to get better acquainted. Paris comes straight over and sits next to me and introduces herself. She's all over me pulling my top up to feel my abs, showing her friends my watch (a nice Breitling I had picked up that week). Anyway it's pretty obvious this girl is keen as fuck for a bit of naughtiness; it's always in their eyes. Meanwhile all the boys are working their magic on Paris's mates. She straddles me and we start kissing. She only has this really short skirt on which is hiding nothing, in full view of everyone, but as far as they can see it's just gentle flirting. So we are kissing etc. Now I've only been talking to her for half an hour tops. So imagine my surprise when she starts unbuttoning my jeans, bit controversial this with everyone around. But I'm arseholed so not really caring too much, so she starts undoing my jeans like I said but lifts her skirt down as far as it will go so you can't really see. So she starts wanking me off, fucking brilliant, I couldn't believe it. I'm trying not to laugh as I'm sure my mates are going to see. It gets better though: the next thing is she's pulling her knickers to the side and putting my cock in her and bold as brass starts riding me. At this point she's warmed me up and as much as I'm thinking this is ridiculous I couldn't care less. At first it was pretty gentle and so we were slipping under the radar, but after a couple of minutes she's really going for it and I was so drunk I had completely forgotten about everyone else. So it's all going swimmingly when suddenly there is a tap on my shoulder. It was one of the doormen who whispers in my ear, "I'm sorry, mate, you're going to have to leave." I looked at him thinking, oh fuck, I'm in trouble here, but the guy has the biggest grin imaginable on his face, and gives me a thumbs up. The only problem is I've got a massive hard-on with my jeans undone inside this girl thinking, how the hell am I going to move without showing anything! Anyways I managed to wriggle out without too many people seeing my baby maker and tell the rest of the lads that I have to go. They have been so engrossed in their own little party that they have been paying no attention whatsoever to what had just happened and are not impressed with me wanting to leave. After impressing upon them the urgency of the situation, i.e. I needed to finish this bird off back at the flat, they begrudgingly agree to my departure. So I manage to get my coat and I see my mates all following behind. They have obviously realised what had just happened and are thinking there is no way I'm leaving this bird with him, as they want to see where this night leads. We get outside to the taxi rank and they catch up with me. They're all saying, "I'm coming with you, I'm coming with you," but I sneak off first in a cab with Paris. We head back to my mate's who lives just over Chelsea Bridge in a penthouse apartment, real nice. So we get back to the flat and get into the lift. She's all over me, absolutely insatiable; quick as a flash I have her half naked and I'm nailing her in the lift. Anyone who had called the lift would have caught us at it. We fell out of the lift, still going at it and get to his flat on the twelfth floor and he's got the bloody keys so I can't get in! So as we are waiting she locks in on me, horny as you like, and starts to fuck me in the hallway under the bright lights outside his flat. After a couple of minutes my mate gets back with the others, opens the lift and sees us there on the floor going hammer and tongs and starts wetting himself and unlocks the door to let us in. At this point she s a little embarrassed as she has been caught shagging naked in a hallway, and goes all shy on me but I'm far from finished with her so I get in and pour us a couple of drinks in the kitchen. I give her a bit of chat and start telling her how gorgeous she is. I get the lads to leave us for a minute so I can warm her up again knowing that we could have some fun with this one, and the boys, trusting me, as usual oblige. After ten minutes or so of some well-chosen words and a couple of lines, the lads come back in and she is in the mood again. We get the music channel on and I start to tell her that she is much better looking than the girls in the music videos and a better dancer too. She's loving the attention and starts to dance for us all. I tell her to take her clothes off and show the boys how gorgeous she is. She says, "No, not in front of these guys," and I said, "Come on, you look so sexy! Plus these are my best mates, and I'm bisexual anyway. In fact it really turns me on watching a girl I fancy get fucked by one of my mates." That was all she needed, she walks up to my mate who owns the flat and starts kissing him with us both watching; next thing I know he has his trousers off and she starts noshing him off. I come up behind her and start fucking her from behind. Anyway the other guy who is watching whilst jerking off and asking for his turn has disappeared and has come back with a video camera and starts filming it. It escalated fairly quickly and we all stripped naked and were taking turns on her whilst filming the whole thing. It was brilliant and she couldn't get enough. It went on about for about two hours, we were all exhausted, sweating our tits off, it was proper messy. After a while I'd had enough so I went to bed in the next room. When I woke up she had gone, left in a taxi. I was made up: there is nothing worse than having to deal with a girl like that the next day. That's why, generally, I make it a rule to get rid of them when you finish. So I walked through to my mate who had disappeared to get the camera and he had a massive smile on his face. I said, "You alright?" He went, "Absolutely bloody brilliant; after you went to bed I fucked her another three times." The dirty bastard, he still waxes lyrical about that night to this day. That poor girl, she got some serious action that night!

5 30-minute dash

After games we would have to head off to some

of the sponsors' boxes and lounges and do some personal appearances. In the players' lounge there would always be loads of glamour girls who want to date a football player along with some of the other minor celebs from London. One of the box holders, Jim, was a top lad, thought of himself as a bit of a gangster, a bit of a wide boy but always had great banter and always looked after the players, so whenever I had to do a box appearance I went to his. He always had his mates in there who were usually a good crack too and he loved entertaining the players' girlfriends or any tidy girls that turned up. This one time one of the injured players brought along two girls to a game, Clare and Nat, right little hotties. If there were friends of the players in the players' lounge they'd often get into a box with free booze and food like I said and we'd all join them after the game. They started coming fairly regularly and had met Jim who loved them and he had them in his box so I would see them after every home game. I had to be careful as my missus would often be in there too so I was always conscious of making a move. This girl Nat was absolutely gorgeous: blonde hair, blue eyes, but there was no way you could really make a move at the ground and certainly not in front of all the other guys' girlfriends so getting her number was a nightmare. Anyways there was this one game, a cup game, and after the game I head up to Jim's box and the girls are there. That weekend my missus hadn't gone to the game, so I was free to make my play as long as I stayed off the radar of the other players' girlfriends. So we had won well and we had a few days off after the game so everyone had arranged to go out after the game into Fulham. We used to go there after games quite a lot and the pubs would always sort us out vodkas and beers for when we rocked up as our presence always brought the rest of the punters in. So I started to talk to the girls, small talk bollocks about the game and stuff, and I drop in that everyone will be heading out and that they should come. They are mad keen so I leave the ground and fly back to Fulham to get changed and head out. I rock up with one of the players to the first bar and fire into the vodkas. After a few, I spot the girls and head over. One of the guys is trying to get hold of Clare leaving me with her mate Nat, perfect. There are loads of people around but I've really got the horn. As the music is playing she's grinding herself against me. The problem is my girlfriend is there as well, so I'm playing it as cool as I can, but she keeps grinding me and rubbing my cock. I can't take anymore so I say to her, "Right, meet me outside in two minutes." She knew I had a girlfriend and had obviously seen her there so she knew why I had made the request. So she disappeared out of the fire exit and I went and found my mate and said, "Give me your keys." After a quick explanation he was happy to hand them over. There was no way I'd go back to mine as my bird's mate was there getting ready to come out and there were far too many people who knew my girlfriend who lived by me.

So I went outside, met her there, jumped into the taxi straightaway and belted it to Battersea where he lived. As soon as we had got into the taxi we were all over each other. She was telling me she had wanted to do this since she had first laid eyes on me; fucking likewise, I thought. I knew I didn't have much time as I had to get back to the flat, snap her back and get back to the bar without my girlfriend or anyone else noticing. This was pushing it even by my standards. So we arrived, ran into the lift, and I started to undress her as soon as the lift door closed. There was a CCTV camera in the lift so I knew the concierge would be able to see everything but he was a top lad and knew what to expect from me. We got into the flat and both got naked. I picked her up and carried her into the bathroom, and we got into the shower. The sex was unbelievable, I absolutely destroyed her. She was screaming the place down, the sexual tension had been building for weeks and it was all coming out now. The clock was ticking and it started to play on my mind but I had unwittingly saved myself five minutes as I was already in the shower. As soon as I'd finished I got out, dried myself off, and told her to get dressed. I was ready almost instantly but her hair was wet and her make-up ruined. I quickly buzzed the concierge who burst out laughing at the sound of my voice, he had obviously enjoyed the show in the lift, and asked him to order two taxis, one as fast as possible and one in fifteen minutes. This was perfect: I could go immediately so I wasn't gone too long and could walk through the door of the bar alone so as not to arouse suspicion, and she had time to dry her hair and redo her make-up, everyone's a winner.

So I leave twenty quid for Nat's taxi and fly downstairs to catch my cab and receive rapturous applause from the concierge. Within thirty-five minutes I was there and back having fucked her. Now that is professionalism for you, a real smash and grab. So I got in through the door of the bar and sure enough my bird ran up to me and asked me if I was alright, was everything okay. I wasn't sure if she was on to me so quickly came up with a counter and said, "Yeah, just been on the phone to my mum, it turns out my aunty has had a heart attack." She was really worried saying, "Is everything alright?" I said, "Yeah, yeah, she'll be alright, just a little shaken, that's all!" That put her straight on the back foot, she totally forgot that I had even been away at all.

6 When twins go wrong

A good friend of mine ran the biggest promotions company in London. He would always look after me and the other footy boys, VIP at all the best nightclubs, and he would always get us tickets to the Brats and any other big events that were happening in London. One day I got a phone call from him telling me that he had got us loads of tickets for this awards do. It was something to do with Nuts magazine or one of the other lads' mags. It was being held in one of the top nightclubs just off Oxford Street. The deal was we showed up, had a few pictures taken with the girls for the mag, and we got as much free booze as we could drink, but a nightclub full of glamour models...are you kidding? I didn't need to be asked twice, put it that way. Anyway we arrived and there were loads of birds there; they were everywhere, Page Three, glamour models it was unbelievable, and they were all in bikinis. As soon as we showed up the girls went wild, as did we and whilst the photos were being taken there was plenty of grappling and flexing. I just couldn't wait to get inside and get started, I was so excited. Now it wasn't a school night so we had a few nights off between training which meant we could get on it, and as it was free booze we were all going for it, the girls too. It was the start of some Internationals and I hadn't been picked so I was definitely getting on the piss! So we were tucking into this booze and causing a nuisance; the drinking games were coming out, body shots, and as these girls get their kit off for a living they weren't shy about playing naked rules. I clocked these twins a little older than me, maybe twenty-six or twenty-seven, they looked like the two birds off Funhouse, short blonde hair, blue eyes, very Swedish-looking birds. I thought, yes they will do, so made my way over to start talking to one of them and she was lovely, really flirty, you could tell she was a party girl, she had that giveaway look in her eye. Anyway, as I was out with all the boys, the night was all about boozing and fucking about, not getting hold of women, so I got her number and arranged to meet up with her another time.

A few weeks later we arranged to meet at a club in the West End, this club which was pumping at the time, it was the place to be, always loads of footballers and glamour girls, the kind of place where you have to get a table. So I rock up at this club on my own to met her and she is there with her sister and her mates, five of them all top of the range model types, and they were all loose already, so I thought I would share the love and I call up my mates to make up the numbers, make a proper night of it. So I convince a couple of them to come down telling them that they won't be disappointed, and when they arrive they certainly are not. So we get right on it. One of my mates had brought an eight of coke with him and everyone is tucking in, especially the girls. We were all just sitting around our table keying it not even bothering to go to the toilet, very silly, ordering champagne, cocktails and vodka. Then she gives me a couple of Es and tells me her and the rest of the girls had been on them all night, so I double drop. I'm off my tits dancing on the dance floor like a mad man, really twisted and I end up dancing with one of the twins thinking it's the one I'm meant to be with so I start kissing her and grinding etc. Anyway I suddenly look at her under the lights and I'm like, shit, I'm snogging the wrong one, so I pull away a little freaked out, still staring at her, trying to work out which one it is, but she grabs cock and carries on kissing me so I just go with it. I carry on going at it, dancing with her and kissing, really going for it. We spent most of the rest of the night on the dance floor fucking about, I'm bouncing off the walls, grabbing her every now and again for a kiss. Anyway about two to three hours later it's coming to the end of the night about 2.30am or so. So I'm on the edge of the dance floor when she walks up to me with her twin sister in tow. She says, "Where we going to go?" I say, "Where do you want to go?" They say, "We don't know, where do you want to take us?" I said, "What, both of you?" She says, "Yeah, as you've been kissing us both all night you may as well fuck us." My jaw dropped, I thought they were kidding, but no, they assured me, I had been kissing them both all night, and that they thought I knew. I couldn't believe it. At the time I was living with my bird, so obviously can't go home. So I suggest a hotel. I'm still amazed, I honestly thought I was only with one of them and wasn't sure if this was a wind-up. But I kept thinking, fuck it, if it's a blag I'll call their bluff. This is too good to ignore, so I was straight on the phone to the hotels.

So we all pile out of the club and I'm having absolutely no joy with hotels at all so I head to this one I know in Hammersmith which is always open late and always lets me in as I've taken a few birds back before and they always open after a bit of chat and a dropsie for the concierge. So we are hammering it at a 1000mph to Hammersmith as I'm horny as fuck, the girls want some beak, so on the way I meet this guy I know and get some off him. Anyway we arrive at the hotel and I walked straight into the guy at the desk and instantly asked for a suite. He looks at me like I've got two heads and says, "I'm sorry, we've only got double beds. How many of you are sleeping in there?" looking at the two girls I'm with, a little smirk on his face. "Just two of us," I said and he said, "But there are three of you." For some reason he couldn't see the potential of what may happen so I told him that the other sister wanted to stay there the following weekend and wanted to just check it out! He laughed at me, but twenty quid later he let all three of us in.

So we all clamber upstairs and to the room. We get in there and strip naked, raid the mini bar and tuck into the coke. It was class, we were having our own little naked party, sniffing lines off each other and then gradually the sex started. I've got them both blowing me at once, them kissing each other, it was the horniest thing I have ever seen. I'm getting excited talking about it now. I must have bolted my load about five times, we just absolutely went for it. We were in the shower, on the floor, everywhere, putting the shower head up them, my cock was so swollen for days after it was a mess we had fucked so much. We got up to all sorts, it was unbelievable sex. I got them to lick each other out, twins! At one point I was doing one from behind whilst she licked out her sister! It was amazing, she just went at her sister's pussy. That said, after four hours one of them freaked out big time, started crying, saying, "I can't believe we've just done that. I can't believe it." In her head she hit the panic button and bolted, leaving me with the other sister in the room and we just slept it off, woke up, snuck out of the hotel and went back to my missus. I never ever saw them again, would you believe!

7 Gymtastic

Myself, along with the rest of the squad, used to get free membership to an upmarket chain of gyms, through the club. We would mainly use the facility for the Jacuzzi and the sauna, for recovery after games, or sometimes to do a light beach weights session on a day off. Sometimes however we would have scheduled team sessions in the gym, both as a change of scenery for the players and as part of the deal the club had with the gym. On this particular occasion it was one of the scheduled team weights sessions. I had been in the gym with the rest of the defence and had done my session. We all then piled into the Jacuzzi for a chill out and to see if there were any decent women about. As I said this was an upmarket gym and in the day was full of rich kept women playing tennis or training whilst their husbands were hard at work. And there were more often than not a few belters in the pool.

So I'm in the Jacuzzi with the rest of the lads and this girl walks in sporting a G-string bikini, in unbelievable shape with a set of fake tits, and starts having a shower in full view of us. We couldn't believe it; it was like watching a live porno. After her shower she walks past us and goes into the sauna. All the lads are going on about how amazing she is and how they would love to shag her, and more for banter than any real desire to get hold of her I said, "I bet you I can get her number now." They all told me to fuck off, 'yeah, whatever', the usual shit, so I said, "Fine," stood up and made my way over to the sauna, with unsupportive remarks ringing in my ears. As I approached I was actually thinking this could go horribly wrong but I was already committed. I walked in and was pleased to see that we were the only two in there, and kicked off with some small talk. After a bit of banter and the revelation that she was a lap dancer, I knew I was in, so I asked her for her number. She said yeah and that she would meet me in the bar to give me her digits. I emerged from the sauna deadpan, no expression on my face, and the lads started heckling me convinced I had been bombed. After telling them the news I still had some doubters, so once we had showered and dressed I had a tableful of football players in the bar waiting to see if I was telling the truth. After a while she came out, came over, got out her phone, looked me straight in the eye and said, "So you just want sex then?" I was slightly taken aback; was this a trick question? I thought fuck it, I'll call her bluff and said, "Well yeah, pretty much." She replied, "Good, because I have a boyfriend. Is that OK with you?" OK with me!! I couldn't believe my luck. This was perfect: a seriously tidy Jack the Ripper has just offered it to me on a plate and told me I can swerve all the nicey nice, I really like you shit. Winner. So we exchanged numbers and I offered her a lift home, which she accepted.

On the way to her house she explained that she lived with her boyfriend and that they were having work done on the house so I would have to drop her off round the corner so none of the workmen saw us. We also arranged to meet in a couple of hours. Now I obviously couldn't go to hers and I didn't want her to know where I lived so mine was out, so I just said that I would surprise her as to where we would go. Later on I returned to where I had dropped her off and collected her. My plan was to drive out of town and either find somewhere for a bit of alfresco or get into a hotel. After driving for about an hour and inspecting a couple of potential outdoor venues, all of which were offside, I was getting seriously impatient, and the fact that she kept rubbing my cock and telling me what she was going to do to me wasn't helping. So I decided that the next hotel we came across I was going in. We didn't come across one for about twenty minutes by which point I was gagging. So when I saw the gates of an expensive-looking hotel I pulled straight in. We parked and made our way to reception. I could tell that this was a serious hotel five-star job, but at this point I was beyond caring and paid £300 for a room for the night.

We got into the room and all the tension was released. I absolutely hammered her up against the wall. She was loving it; she obviously liked it rough and kept asking me to pull her hair when I was fucking her from behind. We were at it for about an hour before we collapsed exhausted on the bed. Now I had the old dilemma of getting rid. I had had my fun and wasn't down for the cuddling after, and then her phone rang. It was her boyfriend, he had been away on business and was going to be home early. Again a gift from above. What a lifesaver this guy was. She panicked, showered and dressed quickly and, with lots of apologies, asked me to take her home. I took her home as quickly as I could for which she was very grateful. What she didn't understand was that I was driving fast for my own benefit, not hers. After dropping her off and promising that we would do it again I was setting off for home when a thought suddenly occurred to me. I had a five-star hotel room for the night including bed and breakfast. I got straight on the phone to one of the lads, picked him up and went back!! We had lovely dinner, had the bed changed in the room to two singles, had a lovely breakfast and went to training the next morning thoroughly relaxed!!

The Conclusion

Firstly, thanks for reading ***'The Seven Worst Men in London'***. Having read all the stories myself for the first time, I wasn't sure if I should have put this book together. Now it's there and on paper, I actually think, what's wrong with people being out there a little sexually; what's wrong with people being complete womanizers? In a world where not being politically correct is more important than, say, being a good person. Or pretending to be noble when underneath you harbour some dark secrets, or at a time when men everywhere are frankly becoming less manly. Something like this is actually quite refreshing; at least it's honest!

I was trying to work out what I'd learnt from this; what I might say when people ask why I put this together. The reason I wanted to do this was because I thought, why not share some of these extraordinary lives with everyone? I then thought of just how many adverts you see on TV where men are emasculated or times when there is a public outcry over men who may be a little too celebrated when it comes to meeting women. The reality is that there is a place for everyone on this planet. Some people like sex more than others; some men want to pick up women like trophies; and some do it just for a good story. Is that wrong? I mean these guys are not doing it against women's will; it is consensual! I'm not sure I want to say wholeheartedly that these guys are amazing, and that everyone should live by their standards. I would like to say, read the stories and take what you want from them. Be a little impressed! A little amazed, a little envious or a little disgusted. As for me, well, I'm amazed at just what an individual can get up to should they so choose.

Many a psychologist will analyse these seven men and try and put them into categories: perhaps they are missing a mother figure in their lives, or perhaps they harbour self-resentment. What if, however, they just like having sex? Aren't men meant to? I know it seems a little cliché to say let a man be a man. It's only our primal instincts, going back to the days when our knuckles dragged on the floor and we lived in caves. Maybe it is, maybe it isn't. As a conclusion this needs to sum up what I thought, so I'll break it down into what I've learnt from these seven men.

The very first thing I noticed between all these guys is just how easy it is for them to meet women. I don't mean at a bus stop or at work. I mean when they want to have sex, pure and simple. They approach women with the express purpose of sleeping with them. If they choose to sleep with them they can, but why? What is the commonality between these men as to why they have so much success? I can imagine people are all looking for this one answer. I know I wish I'd known when I was fourteen years old. I absolutely one hundred per cent dislike the self-help books like 'The Game' or 'The Art of Seduction'. No disrespect to the authors, but they are writing those books so they can set themselves up as experts and continue their sideline of sex seminars, and helping men get more women. They think picking up women is a technique which can be learnt by paying someone $500 and being humiliated for three hours. That is not what being a player or a womanizer, whatever you like to call it, is all about. If you had to have a pinnacle of pulling power, a top of the tree as to who is the best, you won't go far wrong from these seven guys; in fact, I'll place a bet that they are at the top of the sex tree. They haven't been taught by reading books; they don't have to sit in a dark room while some dick tells them to be more empowered. They pull because they know how and because they always have!

I know that these men have techniques; of course they have a particular kind of style. It is however something that shouldn't (or maybe can't) be taught. Everyone should find their own way, should they so desire. I'm amazed that people can be taught to pick up women. But what is more impressive is if you are an inbuilt 'pulling machine'. So back to what I was saying. What is the one common denominator between all these men? Pure and simple: **CONFIDENCE**.

I know it seems a very simple finding, but honestly that is what they all have in common. When you strip back the way they perhaps chat up the women, the way they approach women, or the way they accept knock-backs, the reason they are so successful is confidence, pure and simple. It makes sense if you think about it; what if you really felt like you had nothing to lose when trying to pick up a potential mate? Well, you come across as less desperate for one, for a start! You just have to look at any walk of life from the head of a large multinational to a rugby player strolling onto the pitch to represent his country. They have a belief in themselves that they will succeed. Of course this can wane over time, but the principle is confidence that will help you prosper in anything. Dating, womanizing or even just meeting the fairer sex is exactly that: if you want to do well, it's about confidence.

I think with these seven men it's an inbuilt confidence, possibly from their professions, possibly instilled by their parents; perhaps physical or just something learnt over time. Whatever it is they all have that same ingredient. I bet if you research the various Lotharios through time, Don Juan, Casanova or even Tom Jones, they'll have that same trait: confidence!

In conclusion I hope you've enjoyed what can be only be described as an utterly shameless and frank look into the depraved, secret lives of seven anonymous guys from London. What have we learnt? Well, I suppose that is for you to decide. I've learnt that underneath every glossy photo there is a story to be told. If you want to learn from these men, do! It may be for the technique or it may be for the way you don't want to live your lives. They are, however, 'out-there' characters with a collection of personal stories worthy of rock gods. Considering they are guys like you and me, I'm utterly impressed, thanks to 'the seven worst men in London'.